THE
Father of Canadian Psychiatry
JOSEPH WORKMAN

THE AUTHOR was born in Malawi, Central Africa, and educated in Scotland where she earned a Diploma in Education and an M.A. Honours in Geography and Political Economy, with a teaching specialist certificate in History. In Canada she initially was involved in teaching but switched to Social Work, receiving her M.S.W. in 1963 from the University of Toronto. She worked in several diverse settings, usually in management and teaching positions, most recently at the Children's Aid Society of Metropolitan Toronto. In 1989 she earned the title of Adjunct Practice Professor from the Faculty of Social Work, University of Toronto, and was President for several years of their Association of Field Practice Educators. She has had several articles and speeches published. In 1969 she became the Historian and Archivist of the First Unitarian Congregation of Toronto, and in this role she gave numerous presentations on the topic of Dr. Joseph Workman, for example, at the Annual Workman Lecture series. She is married with two children, and until recently resided in Toronto. Presently she is living in Victoria, B.C.

THE

Father of Canadian Psychiatry
JOSEPH WORKMAN

Christine I. M. Johnston

Christine I. M. Johnston

THE

ogden PReSS

VICTORIA

Published by
The Ogden Press
17 Dock Street, Victoria, B.C., Canada
V8V 1Z9

First Printing: February, 2000
Second Printing: October, 2000

Canadian Cataloguing in Publication Data
Johnston, Christine I. M., 1934 –
Father of Canadian Psychiatry: Joseph Workman
ISBN 0-9686558-0-7
Includes bibliographical references and index.
1. Workman, Joseph, 1805-1894. 2. Psychiatrists–Canada–Biography.
3. Psychiatry–Ontario–History. I. Title.
RC438.6.W67J64 2000   616.89'0092   C99-911355-0
Printed in Canada by the Hillside Press, Victoria, B.C.
Design: Mel Johnston

Contents

Illustrations

ALL the Irish photos were taken by the author in 1992. The map of Toronto was created from data available. Regarding the scenes of Toronto, No. 8 was provided by the Metro Toronto Public Library, and No. 9 from the *Globe and Mail* Archives. All the family photos were provided by John Haynes of Toronto, although institutions such as the Clarke Institute and the First Unitarian Congregation also own copies of some of them. Dates were not available.

1. Home of the Workman family in Ballymacash, Ireland. This was originally a schoolhouse in 1792, one of the first public schools in the north of Ireland.
2. Cottage of the early 19th century showing the original style of the Workman home.
3. Joseph's first school at Mullacarten, now a family home.
4. Dunmurry Non-subscribing Presbyterian Church, attended by the Workman family.
5. Workman pew in the far corner of the church (marked by a plaque).
6. Portrait of the Rev. Dr. Henry Montgomery, located inside the church.
7. 1847 sketch of King Street East in Toronto, showing St. James's Cathedral and the general location of the Workman Brothers Hardware store.
8. Sketch of the Asylum at 999 Queen Street West, around the time it was built in1850.
9. Map of Toronto, 1860: key sites related to Joseph's life.
10. Joseph as a young man.

11. Joseph in his working years.
12. Joseph's official portrait.
13, 14 & 15 Joseph in his senior years.
16. Catharine Workman (maiden name Gowdey), Joseph's mother.
17. Elizabeth Workman (maiden name Wasnidge), Joseph's wife.
18. Dr. Ben Workman, Joseph's eldest brother and Assistant at the Asylum.
19. Dr. Charles K. Clarke, Joseph's student, friend and extended family member.
20. Four of Joseph's children (from left to right, Florence, William, Anna and Fred).
21. The children of William & Jane Workman. Jane was C.K. Clarke's sister and the "Miss Jennie" to whom Joseph wrote, inviting her to the Asylum. The eldest girl, Elizabeth, named after Joseph's wife, was the Bessie who wrote to Joseph on his 87th Birthday. The youngest was named after her great-grandmother, Catharine Gowdey, at Joseph's insistence and with some bribery. She lived, as did her namesake, to a ripe old age. She had collected many of the family memorabilia, which were later given to her grandson, John Haynes. (See Appendix for Family Tree and 87th Birthday Letters.)

Foreword

THE name of Joseph Workman (1805-1894) is familiar to historians of Canadian medicine, especially those pursuing the roots of psychiatry in this country. Other than them, few psychiatrists and fewer members of the general public will recognize the name or the accomplishments. Christine Johnston's biography should help to reduce this unjustified obscurity, expanding, as it does, on Tom Brown's essay in the Dictionary of Canadian Biography.

Workman's career was unusual. It was commonly necessary, for financial reasons, for early practitioners in Canada to follow more than one occupation. For example, Harmaunus Smith practiced medicine in Hamilton and ran a working farm. Robert Kerr, living in what is now Niagara-on-the-Lake, was a private medical practitioner, a judge, a member of the Land Board, Surgeon to the Indian Department, and wore other hats as well. So we should not be surprised to find Joseph Workman doing something similar a generation later.

What is different is that Workman followed his separate careers quite separately. He practised medicine for a few years, then devoted himself entirely to founding and consolidating a hardware business in Toronto (paralleling one his brothers were operating in Montreal). Then, several years later, he apparently left the business world forever. He taught in John Rolph's medical school, and resumed medical practice.

But he was not a general practitioner; his last career was in psychiatry. For three decades as an "alienist," or psychiatrist, Workman shouldered a double load. He sought ways to alleviate the lot of the thousands of Ontarians who were, in the harsh terminology

of the time, labelled "maniacs," idiots," and the like. Simultane-
ously, like all public servants, Workman tried to live within "the
system." For him, the system meant government. He struggled for
some years with a too-large committee of political hacks, later with
a non-medical civil servant of honest intentions but who worked
too much by-the-book for Workman's comfort. Eventually he could
cope no longer, but by then he had changed the face of psychiatry
in Ontario.

Yet he is not widely recognized. Often we seem to be remiss in
acknowledging our roots. Some of Workman's colleagues and students have been treated more kindly by history than has Workman. Charles Kirk Clarke (1857-1924) began his career in psychiatry under Workman in 1874. He worked in asylums in Hamilton, Kingston and Toronto, and, later, was Professor of Psychiatry and Dean of
the Toronto Faculty of Medicine. His name is perpetuated in the
Clarke Institute of Psychiatry. Similarly, Richard Maurice Bucke
(1837-1902), who was head of the London, Ontario, asylum for 25
years beginning in 1877, has remained much in the public eye. Several books have been written about Bucke, and a recent movie has
presented him to a very wide audience indeed. Of course, Bucke has
had the advantage of becoming a disciple of Walt Whitman, his first
biographer, and a literary executor; he also wrote a book on mysti-
cism, *Cosmic Consciousness*, that is in print still, a century after publication

Why do we not emulate London, England, with its famous "blue
plaques" – now more than 600 of them? While we do have some
historical markers we surely need more. Where are the plaques to
identify the site of Workman's home or the hardware business? Is
Dr. Johnston's school in Weston, which gloried in educating William
Osler, identified? Where did Christopher Widmer live or practise?
How about John Rolph, or Elizabeth Bagshaw, or Charlotte Ross
(Manitoba), or, in Niagara-on-the-Lake, Robert Kerr? Dr. William
Case was perhaps the first physician to live and practise in Hamil-

ton, but how would the public know that?

Happily, Johnston helps correct this untoward reticence with respect to at least one pioneer. As she points out, there are in fact a few identifiable traces of Workman's existence in Toronto, though none visible to the man or woman in the street.

A particular strength of *Father of Canadian Psychiatry* is its substantial emphasis on the large Workman family – he was one of nine children, and he and his wife had ten – and on Joseph's activities and interests outside the strictly medical. The result is a breadth of view sometimes lacking in a relatively short biography. Thus the reader will find information not only about 19th century medicine and psychiatry, but also about education (both for medical students and for children), about local politics in Toronto, and about the religious hierarchy of the province, particularly with respect to Unitarianism. The scope is wide-ranging, the presentation satisfying.

CHARLES G. ROLAND, M.D., D.Sc.,
Jason A. Hannah Professor of the History of Medicine,
McMaster University, Hamilton, Ontario.

Acknowledgments

Many people have helped and encouraged me over the past thirty years, for which I am profoundly grateful. Fellow members at First Unitarian Congregation of Toronto enjoyed my anecdotes about Dr. Joseph Workman and encouraged me to write his story. Joan Harris, Dorene Jacobs and Judy Brady were particularly interested in language and helped me with editing. Others were fond of exploring history and provided factual advice, such as Kay and the late Frank Lewis, Bunny Turner, Dr. John Kennedy and the Rev. Chris Raible. Other members of the Historical Committee and the Canadian Unitarian Universalist Historical Society were also most helpful.

The Rev. Phillip Hewett, Minister Emeritus of the Vancouver Congregation and author of several books including *Unitarians in Canada*, has been very supportive over the years. His most recent contribution was in reading an early draft and commenting on the accuracy of historical data. Three retired editors in Victoria offered final editing, namely Diane McLaren, Konnae Harresson and especially Ruth Ralston, and all deserve my gratitude.

During the years of research I have been greatly helped by the staff in the archives I have visited: Queen Street Mental Health Centre Archives; Academy of Medicine Collection (now mostly in the Thomas Fisher Rare Book Library of the University of Toronto, with some articles deposited in the Toronto Hospital Library); the University of Toronto Archives; the Toronto Board of Education Archives; the Toronto City Hall Archives; the Ontario Archives; and the Baldwin Room of the Toronto Reference Library. There has been considerable staff turnover so it is hard to list all the people involved. One person has been outstanding, however: Dr. Cyril Greenland. He and Dr. Jack Griffin have volunteered their time over the past six-teen years to build up the Archives at the Queen Street Mental Health Centre, and have consistently encouraged my research. On one occasion Dr. Greenland even shared his lunch to support my endeavors.

Since writing this biography, a few of the Toronto institutions have merged and restructured. For example, at the beginning of 1998 the Toronto Board of Education and City of Toronto were integrated into new, wider, district organizations, and the Queen Street Mental Health Centre and the Clarke Institute have merged.

The Rev. William McMillan of the Dunmurry Non-subscribing Presbyterian Church was very helpful on my visit to Northern Ireland in 1992, as was the School Principal at Ballymacash and my cousins, Alison and Ralph Spearman of Belfast. (The latter taught at the famous Institute described in Chapter Two and in Ben's Story in the Appendix.)

Several members of the Workman family have been very interested in and supportive of my research. Unfortunately three key people have since passed on. Mary (known as Maidie) Graves of Sharbot Lake and Ottawa, presented me with a small plaster bust of Joseph, so her memory lives on in her gift. Another Workman was Anne Hadley of Toronto, who followed in the direct line of descent from Joseph's eldest son. The third was John Haynes, known also as Jack, of St. Catharine's, Ontario, who guarded and loved the Workman family histories. I remember their contribution with thanks. Luckily several of their children have taken on their parents' interests, namely Nancy Graves Lauder of Kanata and John Haynes of Toronto. John kindly provided boxes of original letters and photographs of Dr. Workman's family. In addition, Judith and Elizabeth St. John were very generous in giving me Dr. Benjamin's diary and details of the Bascom side of the family.

Lastly, I must thank my husband, Mel, without whose help this book would never have been written. His interest, support, tolerance, and his technical typographic skills were irreplaceable.

Chronology of the Life of
Dr. Joseph Workman

1805 Born on May 26th, at Ballymacash, near Lisburn, west of Belfast, Northern Ireland.

1829 Emigrated with parents to Montreal, Canada.
Taught at the Union School, owned by brother Benjamin.

1830 Entered McGill University Medical School.

1835 Graduated in Medicine.
Married Elizabeth Wasnidge.

1836 Moved to Toronto and managed the Wasnidge hardware store.

1837 Licensed to practise medicine in Upper Canada.

1840 Opened Workman Brothers Hardware Store.

1845 Helped establish Toronto Board of Trade.

1845 Helped establish First Unitarian Congregation of Toronto.

1846 Opened a family practice in Toronto.
Lectured at Dr. Rolph's School of Medicine, Toronto, in diseases of women and children, midwifery,and *materia medica*.

1847 Elected City Alderman in St. David's Ward (involved in health, education and finances).
Started Emigrant Hospital with the help of Toronto General Hospital.

1849 Appointed to Royal Commission to investigate finances of King's College and clergy lands.

1850 Elected first Chairman, Toronto Board of Education.

1853 Appointed Superintendent of the Toronto Lunatic Asylum, interim in 1853 and permanent in 1854.

1855 Toured Asylums in U.S.A. (New England).

1859 Returned to Ireland, and visited asylums in England andFrance.

1875 Retired from the Toronto Asylum, to his house at 113 Mutual Street, Toronto.
Continued forensic consultation work around Ontario.
Continued to translate and write articles for medical journals.
1876 Examined in obstetrics and medicine for the Medical Council.
Elected President of the Canadian Institute.
1877 Elected President of the Canadian Medical Association.
1878 Elected President of the Toronto Medical Society.
1881 Elected President of the Ontario Medical Association.
1892 Celebrated 87th birthday.
1894 Died on Sunday, April 15th, at home in Toronto.

Introduction

Dr. Joseph Workman caught my attention in 1969 when I became the historian and archivist of the First Unitarian Congregation of Toronto. Not only was he the key founder of our organization in 1845, but I discovered that he had participated in the establishment of several important institutions in the city which were still in existence as of December, 1998. These were the Board of Trade, the Toronto Board of Education, the University College of the University of Toronto, Queen Street Mental Health Centre, the Canadian and Ontario Medical Associations, and Toronto Medical Society. He also made a major contribution to asylum management, medical education (in particular, the resident training program), and to research, especially in psychiatry.

The Workman Lectures were started at the church in 1965 to commemorate the key founder. Well-known speakers were invited from across Canada and the States, and occasionally from places as far away as Northern Ireland. Beginning in 1977 the program included a five minute introduction to Dr. Workman, connecting his life to the theme of the speaker. Thereafter, my research into his activities and writings escalated, and I seldom found a theme about which Dr. Workman had nothing to say. Many of the quotations ring true for the twentieth century, because he was ahead of his time and explored ideas still relevant today.

The mid-nineteenth century may seem very far away but many of the concerns prevalent then remain current, such as those related to health: the relationship between poverty and disease; the value of fresh air, good food, exercise and employment; the dangers of overwork; and the causes of mental illness. Others are associated with education: non-sectarian religious education in public schools and at the university level; and teaching people, including women, to think for themselves. Some themes are exemplified by the contributions of the extended Workman family, such as the role played by immigrants. A large number of the issues raised relate to the responsibilities of citizenship: applying social justice and liberal religious principles to social responsibility and social action; standing up to unjust authority; exploring the role of the press; analyzing the causes of crime; and questioning whether capital punishment is a deterrent. Dr. Workman had mixed feelings about the role of politics. His important position at the precursor of Queen Street Mental Health Centre was partly a result of patronage, yet, for most of his life, he fought political interference. He strongly supported public institutions, inspected by trained civil servants. For him, the issue of contention was the decision-making process. Did the professional in charge, the accountant, the inspector or the politician make the key decisions?

Several important historians and medical doctors over the past 150 years have described Dr. Joseph Workman as one of the most eminent and one of the best loved doctors of the nineteenth century. In our day we still need heroes. He had qualities and values we could well emulate today: perseverance and tenacity of purpose tied in with a social conscience, self discipline, a sense of humour, and warmth and loyalty to family and friends. He was interested in and able to inspire the young. He was also aware of his own limitations and frailties, admitting his ignorance on several occasions.

Because of the scarcity of material regarding Workman's early childhood and youth, much use is made of the diary of his older brother, Benjamin. This provides a rich source of information regarding the conditions and family situation in Ireland and Montreal. In 1992 I visited Ireland (and in particular, Ballymacash and Dunmurry), met people connected to the Workmans, and studied relevant local documents available. Regarding the later periods of Workman's life in

Montreal and Toronto, much collateral material as well as his own writings has been preserved. Getting acquainted with this man's life has been a fascinating experience.

There are several Workman family members, including Dr. Ben Workman, involved with the Unitarians and the Queen Street Mental Health Centre, and so Dr. Joseph Workman is frequently and affectionately known as Joseph. In the text, I have called him Joseph rather than Workman.

CHAPTER ONE

Irish Roots and Family Traditions
(1618 - 1805)

"The land came from the devil and it went back to him."
J.W.

DR. Joseph Workman is "thickskinned" and an "irascible, implacable despot!"

These were severe words with which to label a local psychiatrist in the *Globe* of Toronto, the largest newspaper of its day in Canada West. They were written in 1857 by George Brown, the *Globe's* editor and a future Parliamentary leader.[1] He was describing a court battle between Dr. Workman and a disgruntled, former employee. Yet Dr. Joseph Workman withstood the onslaught, fought back with equal vigour, and survived to win honour and fame. He even managed to maintain his popularity with the general public, by relying on his inner strength and courage.

Joseph had been inspired throughout his youth by stories of his ancestors, and one hero immediately comes to mind: the Rev. William Workman, his great-great-great-great grandfather, a clergyman in seventeenth century England. When a friend and publisher, George Rose, wrote up the life story of Joseph in 1888 for his *Cyclopedia of Canadian Biography*, he began with the Rev. William Workman of Gloucester. Indeed, two-thirds of the content was about Joseph's ancestors! This lack of balance reveals Rose's taste for history and his awareness that the readers of the time identified with the "old country" and its legends. It also reveals Joseph's attachment to his roots and his inclination to tell these stories to his friends because they were such formative influences in his life.

"Heretic! Guilty of damnation!" This was a damning accusation to be levelled at an Anglican minister by Archbishop Laud of seventeenth century England. For the previous fifteen years (1618-1633) the Rev. William Workman had been the lecturer at St. Stephen's Episcopal Church in Gloucester, a large town situated in the Severn valley of central England, not far from Stratford-on-Avon. A wise and pious man, he was concerned about the recent edicts advocating the setting up of statues and pictures in the churches, feeling that this practice encouraged a tendency to idolatry and was contrary to the practice of the early Christian church. He was not a man to deny his convictions so he preached his opinions from the pulpit, questioning the legality of the edicts. Someone reported him to William Laud, a former Dean of the Gloucester Diocese, who recently had been appointed Archbishop of Canterbury. The Archbishop was the creator of the new edicts and he was not one to tolerate criticism. Wiping out Puritanism and "anti-establishment heresy" was a chosen mission in his life. The Rev. Workman was brought before a Court of the High Commission, and following a short trial, was convicted of heresy, excommunicated and imprisoned. In addition, he was forced to recant. According to the family history, he was made to kneel before St. Stephen's with his ear nailed to the door, for listening to heresy.[2]

Beaten but not cowed, the Rev. Workman later quietly opened a school for young people. The Archbishop, however, had prohibited him from teaching, in the belief that all education must be controlled by the Anglican Church. So the Rev. Workman switched to a form of medicine in which he had some skill, but the righteous Archbishop, having become Charles I's right-hand man, had the power to forbid even that activity. Every person has his breaking point. Following this latest crushing blow, the Rev. Workman fell into a deep depression and died, leaving behind a large family.[3] Archbishop Laud reaped his own reward, for an angry mob of middle- and working-class people persuaded the English Long Parliament to impeach him, and he was beheaded at the Tower of London for his political activities, on the grounds of treason.[4]

The Rev. Workman's death amidst such tragic circumstances made a deep impression on his children and on his later descendants. Some families forget their roots, but not the Workman family. Right up to the present day many of them have been nursed on the heroic anecdotes of their ancestors. Dr. Joseph Workman's father recounted the tales to his children. Today, twenty-two of Dr. Joseph Workman's great-great-grandchildren have a bust of Joseph adorning their homes. They are following in the steps of Joseph by remembering and identifying with their ancestors and family traditions. The lives of Joseph and the Rev. Workman display similar themes: promoting freedom of thought in religion; speaking out against injustice; becoming a teacher of the young; and practising medicine as a way of translating a social conscience into action. Joseph went one step further. Rather than being a victim of life's injustices, he aided those beaten down and in need.

Following this negative experience in England, the children of the Rev. William Workman moved to Ireland. They felt angry and victimized by their father's untimely death in 1633. The boys joined the Parliamentary Army and one of them, named William after his father, worked his way up to the rank of Captain, serving with Cromwell's Army in Ireland in 1648 and 1649. Cromwell rewarded him liberally "with the goods of other people" for "helping him cut the throats at Drogheda and elsewhere."[5] But the land that had been bought with blood proved too controversial to keep. The Captain later relinquished any legal claims to the land that had been given him, and the family went into milling. To quote Joseph in his telling of the story: "The land came from the devil and it went back to him."[6]

The Workman family of the seventeenth century were Protestants at war with the Irish Catholics who viewed them as English colonists, but by 1800 the situation had changed, and the Workman family had become Presbyterians who were allied with the Catholics against the ruling Anglican hierarchy. So it is not surprising that Joseph, an Ulster Protestant, chose, years later in Toronto, to write editorials for an Irish Catholic newspaper. The owners viewed him as a friend.

The family tree and other stories of the Workman family in Ireland and in the U.S.A. can be found in the Appendix. Of particular importance to Joseph was his father's sojourn in Philadelphia immediately following the American War of Independence. His father and his Uncle Benjamin, had been living in Ireland, but decided to emigrate to the States. Being skilled teachers, they soon became involved in teaching at what was to become the University of Pennsylvania. They met and were influenced by both Benjamin Franklin and George Washington, so Joseph and his siblings were raised on the Yankee free-wheeling spirit along with the traditional values of loyalty to the monarchy and motherland.

The father, Joseph Workman, Senior, remained in the States for just three years, feeling somewhat homesick and complaining of poor health. In 1790 he returned to Ireland, where he immediately found a teaching position in Milltown, in the parish of Derryaghy, located west of Belfast and close to Lisburn. In September, 1792, he transferred to the newly-opened school at Ballymacash, a village nearby. A year and a half later he married Catharine Gowdey, a woman of Scottish descent, who was ten years his junior. The bride's father, Alexander Gowdey, was working for the same employer as himself, namely the Rev. Philip Johnson, Vicar of Derryaghy and one of the small landowners living in the vicinity. Mr. Gowdey was the Land Steward who collected the rents and managed the financial affairs of the estate (which he did for twenty-nine years). The Rev. Johnson was a strong minded and colourful individual, a mixture of progressive and conservative ideas. One of his most memorable actions was to start one of the earliest public schools in the north of Ireland, even before there were any in Belfast.[7] The new, one-room schoolhouse was built for the local children in 1792. It was situated close to the vicar's home, and far from any town. He hired Joseph Workman, Senior, to be the teacher.

Unfortunately after a few years, Mr. Gowdey, the Land Steward, became ill and died, and his son did not have his father's aptitude. The Rev. Johnson was impressed by Joseph Workman, Senior, and asked him to handle the financial business in addition to his teaching job. The financial role expanded as the landowner's estate increased in size. As time went on the Workman family also increased in size, and as a result, so did the financial obligations faced by Workman. Subsequently, the experimental school was closed down, the schoolhouse converted into the Workman family home, and Workman devoted his full attention to managing the Johnson estate. Both men felt guilty about the closing of the school, so eventually another building was erected and the school reopened with a new teacher.

For thirty-five years, Joseph and Catharine Workman lived in Ballymacash, raising nine children, eight of whom were boys. Dr. Joseph Workman was their fourth son. There was something special about that home because five of the boys went on to fame and fortune in the New World.

CHAPTER TWO

Joseph's Formative Years in Ireland
(1805-1829)

"Walked in all kinds of weather and thought nothing of it."
J.W.

JOSEPH, the fourth son, was born on May 26, 1805. He did not keep a diary of his childhood, or write much about it in later life. Quotations as given above, were spoken later to friends who recorded them. Luckily Benjamin, the oldest of the siblings, wrote about their childhood in Ireland, and this, together with other records, does give a picture of what life was like for the young Joseph. Benjamin had to struggle to complete his education to become a teacher, because money was limited at that time and his father was placing pressure on him to serve an apprenticeship in the linen industry.

Joseph, on the other hand, was encouraged to attend school, but he did have to walk the four miles to the Mullacarten school "in all kinds of weather, and thought nothing of it."[1] His brother Benjamin was the teacher in this one-room schoolhouse, and he was to play a dominant role in Joseph's life. In addition to the classroom teaching, the long walks with Ben were very educational experiences, for the talkative Ben loved to share his knowledge and observations. Daily they trudged through the countryside, reading the weather signals and enjoying the vistas of the valley and hills.

Joseph's position as the fourth son was probably a key factor in his development. He learned to share and take knocks and bumps. Initially, as we shall see, he followed in the footsteps of his older brothers but later found his own direction in life. He also learned to be protective of his younger siblings, developing a strong attachment to his younger brother Thomas (see the family tree).

After the Mullacarten school, Joseph went to Charles Shields's School in Lisburn and finally to the Academy of Benjamin Neely and Son, also in Lisburn. When he was fourteen, he experienced the emigration of his older brother Benjamin, a significant loss in his life. The siblings considered following Ben to Canada if his reports of the new land proved favourable, and even the parents contemplated eventual retirement in Canada. Meanwhile the father had taught his remaining sons the rudiments of surveying, one of his many skills, so it seemed natural that four years later Joseph would follow two older brothers, Alexander and William, into ordnance surveying.

By age twenty-one Joseph had done so well that he was appointed to a responsible position on the Ordnance Survey of Ireland and worked there for three years. He enjoyed the work, later commenting that he always regarded that period of his life as having afforded him the best part of his education. It is unlikely that Joseph said this lightly, for he did not see education as being solely academic learning. He felt true education meant observing and reasoning for oneself. Certainly this job helped develop his powers of observation, highlighting the connection of cause and effect in the weather, and provided ample opportunity for star-gazing and bird-watching. Joseph's Weather Diaries (1860-1894) became an important part of his life, and were of interest to later generations.[2]

There must have been something unique about the upbringing of the Workman children that helped them contribute so richly in later life to the development of Canada. Certainly the two instrumental figures were the parents. Joseph Senior was an unusually well-educated and well-travelled man, undoubtedly extremely intelligent. He did not want his sons to become teachers, for he thought the financial rewards were too meagre. Catharine was a caring, intelligent, ambitious and energetic woman who enjoyed excellent health and lived to be one hundred and two years old. Her children loved and admired her, and her son Joseph later called her "his dearest friend."[3] Yet she was strict. Another of the sons, Alexander, told his nephew (Joseph's son, Thomas) that he himself used to avoid her switch by dodging through the yew trees at the front entrance of their cottage.[4]

The children grew up with a strong sense of religious and social values, where "moral obligations," Christian charity, and hard work were held in high esteem. The parents, however, also seemed flexible and able to work with those who differed on religious grounds. For example, the Rev. Philip Johnson was an Anglican; one of the father's best friends was a Roman Catholic; and the Workman family attended the Dunmurry Presbyterian Church of the Non-Subscribing tradition.[5] Tolerance was preached there, but also the ability to stand up for one's beliefs in often unpopular causes. Later on all the sons supported controversial issues such as free and non-sectarian education, public health and sanitation, cooperative banking, and the temperance movement. They combined business, education and politics in various blends. A certain puritanical streak can be seen throughout, a strong belief in hard work and self-discipline, as well as a certain ambition. Joseph and Benjamin became doctors, and three others, Alexander, William and Thomas, became very wealthy businessmen involved in politics. Alexander and William ended up as mayors of Ottawa and Montreal respectively and Thomas was elected to the House of Commons.

An entry in Benjamin's diary conjures up a certain picture of their upbringing: "In the days of my childhood my father was sober, industrious and kind. The scenes of domestic happiness which I witnessed in that household have not been surpassed by anything I have met with in the course of my reading. The duties of the school were punctually attended to. The Sabbath never found him absent from his place of worship. His evening hours were devoted to his family, while reading the Scriptures and singing a hymn generally closed the evening's exercises. I have often sat by the fireside table and listened to my Father and Mother singing this hymn: 'If solid happiness we prize, Within our breast this jewel lies.' In that young family there was true happiness and true religion: peace was there, piety was there. Love to God and Love to Man were there, and it was recognized by all the neighbourhood ... As Grandfather and Grandmother Gowdey lived about half a mile from our residence, we frequently enjoyed the pleasure of their company of a Sabbath evening, and this interchange seemed to cast new life into the domestic scene."[6]

In another section of Ben's diary, Joseph Workman, Senior, was described as being a relatively gentle person, and an avid reader and conversationalist. Ben went on to say: "I well remember how assiduous my Father was in storing my young mind with knowledge. His verbal teachings concerning God, Christ, Heaven and a future existence are yet fresh in my memory and have been I think the basis of my moral course in life. He was always very careful to impart to me the leading facts of Astronomy, of the structure of the solar system ... and doctrine of attraction as promulgated by Newton."[7] Joseph later said that they were raised also on the teachings of George Washington and Benjamin Franklin, with republican sentiments well mixed with loyalty to the Crown.

Ballymacash, the hamlet where the Workman family lived, remains a small village strangely set in the middle of a modern housing estate. The Rev. Johnson's large, impressive, grey stone house still sits in well-groomed grounds. At a crossroads nearby, the modest Workman family cottage, now two hundred years old, has been converted into a small commercial site.

By today's standards their home seems small for a large family. It is a long, low, white-washed building with no grace or style. Yet according to family records and photos, it had looked rather welcoming in past years, enveloped as it was by flowering hawthorn bushes with a big yew tree by the gate.[8] The children spent much time out-of-doors exploring the local countryside. Ballymacash was then mostly farms, fields and woods, surrounded by low and rolling hills, allowing for travel in all directions. The nearest big centre, Lisburn, was within walking distance and was frequently visited.

The city of Belfast was twenty miles to the east, but the family made the trip regularly on Sundays when the children were older, travelling to the small town of Dunmurry, on the outskirts of Belfast. The minister there was a famous preacher, the Rev. Henry Montgomery, and the Workmans were attracted to his teachings. He was the leader of the Irish Presbyterian liberal wing, which was known as the "new light" movement. The leader of the traditional "old light" Calvinists was named the Rev. Henry Cooke. The two groups had co-existed peacefully for a hundred years until this time. Indeed wider issues, such as surviving the persecution by the Established Church (Church of England), had brought all the smaller Protestant and Roman Catholic groups into a friendly coalition. The Church of England was dominated by the ruling classes and protected by the legal system. Its members tended to associate religious liberty with the republicanism so rampant in the south of Ireland, in France, and in the U.S.A., and so they tried to control the situation by persecuting the minorities.

In the 1820s the "old light" Calvinists produced a talented orator, Henry Cooke from the Presbyterian Congregation of Killyleagh, who wished to exclude all the followers of the liberal "new light" movement from the Irish Presbyterian Church. Henry Montgomery was also a great orator, and not willing to give in easily. He called himself an Arian, which meant that he did not believe in predestination or the stricter tenets of the orthodox Calvinists.[9] For example, he believed in One God (the Father), and one Mediator (Christ), who reconciled man to God by inspiring repentance leading to God's forgiveness. (Initially Montgomery was reluctant to call himself a Unitarian because Joseph Priestley of England called himself a Unitarian, and Priestley was more humanistic and radical than Montgomery.) But this theological reasoning was too liberal for the evangelical Rev. Henry Cooke, who managed to have Montgomery expelled from the official Presbyterian Church. Montgomery and his followers then established the Non-Subscribing Presbyterian Church of Ireland of which the Remonstrant Synod of Ulster was the largest and best known. The name came from their resistance to subscribe to the Westminster Confession, for they believed strongly in freedom of thought in religion. Many of them later accepted the name Unitarian, and joined in association with the British Unitarians. The antagonism between Montgomery and Cooke had been building for several years before the actual split came in 1829.

The break coincided with the departure of the rest of the Workman family for Canada. They had been planning to leave once Joseph, Senior, reached retirement age. They found depressing and discouraging the poverty and the poor harvests of 1818 and 1820, which were forerunners to the terrible 1848 famine. The religious strife only exacerbated the situation and made emigration more attractive. The parents saw no great future for their gifted children in Ireland, though Montgomery remained, keeping in touch with the Workmans. He wrote a testimonial for Joseph, Senior, to use in the New World, which he called a Disjunction Certificate.[10] He even selected the first Unitarian minister in Montreal. Joseph spoke of Montgomery as having had an important influence on his religious thinking. Interestingly, he did not deviate much from Montgomery's philosophy throughout his life, suggesting that he was not just following in the family tradition but had chosen the Unitarian faith for himself.

A brief history of the Royal Belfast Academic Institute is of relevance here, because of its connections with the Workmans and other leading figures in Canada. Prior to 1810 the six northern counties did not have a university, despite the fact that the population was as large as that of Scotland, which boasted four universities. The well-to-do merchants and liberal Presbyterians finally persuaded the British government to set up a non-sectarian centre of learning. Thus in 1810 the Institute was set up to provide both a grammar school and a college education. Benjamin taught there briefly but resigned because of an unfortunate experience with the Principal's wife, in which she betrayed her anti-Irish prejudices. (For details see Ben's story in the Appendix.) Later Henry Montgomery, in addition to his ministerial duties, became for twenty-two years the Headmaster of the English School, one of the sections of the Institute. After Montgomery's appointment, the residence for the English School was located at Dunmurry, suggesting a certain blurring of boundaries between the church and the school. Then in 1840 Montgomery was promoted to Theological Professor at the Institute, despite the protestations of Henry Cooke, and in 1849 the college section evolved into Queen's University, Belfast.[11]

In 1821 another well-known Non-Subscribing Presbyterian, Thomas Dix Hincks, was appointed Head of the Classical School at the Institute. This great scholar also had an influence on the development of Canada, for he fathered Sir Francis Hincks, who became Premier of Canada West, and the Rev. William Hincks, who was a trained Unitarian minister as well as the first professor of Natural History at the University of Toronto. The Workmans and the Hincks brothers came to the New World just as a new era was opening up in Canada.

Some quirk of fate occurred to bring the Workmans to Canada instead of joining their close relatives in the U.S.A. Benjamin described this event in his diary. When he was booking his passage to North America in 1819, he decided to check out the captains of the four vessels about to leave Belfast, before deciding which ship he would take. The captain of the boat destined for New Orleans had just taken "a heavy dose of grog" and did not appear to be "a safe and reliable navigator;" the New York boat had a Mate who blasphemed profusely; and the Philadephia crew were "careless to visitors," ignoring Ben's questions. So he approached the one remaining boat. Samuel Ball, Captain of the *Sally* of Maryport, bound for Quebec, was all that Ben desired. Thus he sailed to Canada rather than to the U.S.A., later remarking that this was "providential," because yellow fever prevailed in all the American ports that summer.[12]

Because Ben came to Canada, all the Workman family came to Canada. Doubtless, if Montreal had not appeared inviting, they would have moved south. Montreal was beginning to fill up with Irish and Scots, and Ben felt relatively comfortable settling there. Yet it is often on such circumstantial happenings that major decisions get made! Ben was the only Workman to record the details of his departure and his feelings at the time of embarkation. Every scene was vivid in his mind. His thoughts probably reflect the sentiments of many emigrants: "The home of my childhood was out of my sight never again to be seen by me. Perhaps there is not a more poignant sensation of the mind than that of parting with all those early connections which bind the Earth."[13]

CHAPTER THREE

Montreal and Cholera
(1829-1836)

"Death's carnival was not complete and his devastations were
now extended beyond the habitations of the indigent
and the houseless."
J.W.

THE Workmans escaped from poverty, poor potato harvests, typhus and religious strife, only to face a cholera epidemic and other crises soon after arriving in Canada. They must have wondered at first if they should ever have left home.

As mentioned, the first of the Workmans to arrive in Canada was Benjamin, ten years ahead of his parents and young Joseph. His first impressions in 1819 were not positive. A snow-clad hill in Cape Breton both astounded and depressed him. He was already feeling discouraged since he had conscientiously nursed several fellow passengers on board the *Sally* who were sick with measles and seasickness, yet none of them had thanked him for his efforts. Quebec City did not inspire him either. The "tawny ... sallow yellow complexions, the lack of culinary vegetables," and the lack of English speakers in this "medieval city" made him decide not to tarry there for even one night. Yet initially Montreal was not a great success either. He found a teaching position almost immediately, but the owner absconded with all the funds, and the bailiffs turned Benjamin out onto the street.[1] Luckily he had already so impressed several parents and friends with his teaching skills that they established a unique school called the Union School, with Benjamin as the Headmaster, on the corner of Craig St. and the Champs de

Mars. By May, 1820, there were one hundred and twenty pupils. It continued till 1845. Its uniqueness was that girls were admitted, though they were taught separately by a female teacher. The Union School fulfilled an unmet need in the city for quality education, and several famous people attended.[2] In 1824 Benjamin became the sole owner, so could offer a teaching position to his brother, Alexander, as well as to young Joseph when he arrived in 1829. Indeed he virtually handed over responsibility for the school to his brothers in 1829, when he began a new career as co-owner and editor of a newspaper, the *Canadian Courant.*

Alexander, the second brother, had emigrated from Ireland in 1820. At first he decided he preferred farming to teaching, so moved on up the Ottawa river to the new township of Huntley. Although he obtained the land for practically nothing, it was backbreaking labour to clear the hundred acres of bush. He persevered for three years and then sold it for $100. He returned to Montreal to join Benjamin at the Union School.[3] Benjamin welcomed him warmly. He took over the running of the school at the time Joseph became a teacher there.

Initially, Benjamin was very lonely in Montreal because when he sought out new friends, he took great care to associate only with those who held sympathetic religious views. Finding no "new light" Presbyterian or Unitarian church to attend, he decided to attend a traditional church and chose the St. Gabriel Street Presbyterian. A few years later a Margaret Manson became the female teacher at his school, and in 1823 they were married. The following year they bought out the other members of the Union School Committee and moved the classes to St. Nicholas and St. Sacrament. In 1827 three of his younger brothers arrived, Samuel (aged only sixteen), Thomas (aged fourteen), and Francis (aged twelve), after a perilous voyage in which their ship narrowly escaped disaster. The young married couple took on the role of parents. The following year John (aged twenty-four) immigrated with his wife. The rest of the siblings, Joseph, William and Ann, arrived with the parents in 1829. Joseph, Senior, now sixty-eight years old, had finally retired.

Joseph later described the voyage as taking five weeks to cross the Atlantic. He himself did not elaborate on the ordeal that this trip represented. From other histories, novels and Ben's diary, we have an image of overcrowding, seasickness, the spread of infectious diseases, the lack of a balanced diet, et cetera, especially for those not rich enough to afford special accommodation. Joseph did record, however, the arrival of their ship, the *Saladin*, on May 15, at the city of Quebec. Two days later there was a big family reunion at Alexander's home in Montreal. Then, on July 14, Ben's wife died. This was the first of several personal tragedies to hit the Workmans. Next on August 22, his brother, John, died of a fever.[4] This had a shattering effect on the whole family, augmented by Ben's also catching the disease, although fortunately he recovered. Soon afterwards Joseph decided to study medicine. His final research thesis was on cholera, another epidemic soon to hit the city. None of the family had practised medicine since the Rev. William Workman tried to do so in 1632. These two sudden deaths happened at a turning point in Joseph's life and became a key motivating factor.

Joseph certainly had ambition, self discipline, stamina and a fervent thirst for knowledge. He was busy all day teaching English Grammar, Classics, and Mathematics. Since he had had no previous experience in teaching, this must have been an exhausting challenge in itself. Then the following year and for the next four years his spare time was spent attending lectures at the General Hospital, and being apprenticed to Dr. John Stephenson as a private pupil. Medicine was in its infancy in Canada and at that time it was the only way to become a doctor. At the age of thirty Joseph completed his training. It was 1835 and he was one of the first doctors to graduate in Canada, his degree granted by the fledgling McGill University. His key teacher, Dr. Stephenson, had been trained in Edinburgh, and after emigrating, had started a Medical Institute at the Montreal General Hospital in 1822. While working in that institution he was granted a dual professorship in Anatomy at the newly founded McGill University. Another of his specialties was midwifery.[5] Joseph became particularly interested in the latter and in the diseases of women and children, in addition to his earlier interest in cholera. In later years Joseph spoke of Dr. Stephenson warmly as someone it was his "highest ambition to imitate," and to whom he felt "the most sincere feelings of gratitude." It is therefore not surprising that he dedicated his medical thesis on cholera to his mentor.[6]

The city of Montreal was a larger urban centre than Joseph was accustomed to. In 1829 it was already a city of about forty thousand, and, as one writer has said: "... an impressive city as North America regarded populations in the middle years of the nineteenth century, but visitors were surprised to find how small a space the city occupied. Its population was mostly crowded into the few streets that had been enclosed by the fortifications erected under French rule. This crowding together ... recalled the medieval cities of Europe. The impression was increased by the narrowness of the streets, some little more than lanes ... Montreal's medieval mood was increased still further by being a city of stone. Many of the buildings dated back to the seventeenth and eighteenth centuries and had been constructed with fieldstone ... The buildings stood right by the sidewalks side by side, without any airy separation ... Some streets, for long stretches, had only the blank, high, grey stone walls of nunneries or monasteries. Greyness was everywhere ... One visitor commented 'Montreal is extremely heavy and gloomy.' "[7] Open sewers ran down the middle of the street. In such a city cholera travelled fast. It started in the immigration sheds by the river, and if people were obviously ill they remained there. But others were to succumb later once they had settled in the city. The fever outbreak of 1829 was a minor one in comparison to the cholera epidemics of 1832 and 1837. In 1832 ten per cent of the population died. Joseph observed that the cholera was infectious and he connected the epi-

demic to poor water supplies and poverty. This was progressive thinking in an age when church leaders were saying that it was God's punishment on mankind for their collective sins.[8]

At first the disease attacked the poor, especially the poverty stricken
Irish immigrants. Joseph described the scene in poignant language:
"Death was at every dwelling" and hundreds of children were or-
phaned "without a morsel to eat and without a shelter wherein to lay
their heads ... all ties of nature torn asunder." The city had become
"one scene of mourning and misery." By midsummer it appeared
again, this time attacking and decimating the wealthy. Joseph commented: "Death's carnival was not complete and his devastations were
now extended beyond the habitations of the indigent and the
houseless."[9] Joseph spent many hours at the immigration sheds aided
by Adam Ferrie, an older man from Scotland, a Unitarian already
active in several humanitarian activities in the city. They covered themselves in sulphur, believing this would protect them against the disease. This resulted in a careful wash and a change of clothes immediately afterwards and it was probably the latter activities which saved
their lives. This is the first recorded occasion of Joseph's charitable
activities. In contrast, his brother, William, fled the city.

When the cholera returned in 1834, people seemed more aware of
the contagious nature of the disease, and precautions were taken such
as quarantine procedures and improvements to the general public
health. This lesson was not lost on Joseph. The relationship between
poverty and poor health was an issue for which he fought when a city
alderman in Toronto and again in his years as an asylum superintendent. Like all the Workman children he had been raised to respect
hard work and wealth, but this always seemed to be tempered by a
sympathetic awareness of people's pain and a strong sense of responsibility to help others, especially the poorer classes.

When Joseph finished his medical studies he was eager to get married. He and his bride chose the St. Gabriel Street Church for the
ceremony, because there was no Unitarian Congregation yet in Mon-

treal. On May 30, 1835, he married Elizabeth Wasnidge, the eldest daughter of Michael and Ann Wasnidge. She also had immigrated in 1829, coming with her family from Sheffield, England, where her father had a thriving business selling penknives and razors. (Their name was also spelt Wasinge, supposedly of French origin.) Her family were Anglicans but for some unknown reason they attended the St. Gabriel St. Presbyterian Church, also known as the Scotch Kirk. Unfortunately, earlier in 1835, her father, Michael, had died of cholera. Her mother planned to take the family to Toronto where her eldest son had established a hardware business. Elizabeth was scheduled to go with her so Joseph quickly proposed and they were wed five days after his graduation. The following year, however, her brother, William, had a fatal accident in Toronto. Mrs. Wasnidge, Senior, was having difficulty running the store, and her younger sons were still adolescents. Probably Joseph was being dutiful but perhaps part of him was interested at trying his hand at the hardware business like several of his brothers. The outcome was that Joseph gave up his fledgling medical practice, bid Montreal farewell and in 1836 moved with his wife to Toronto, taking over William Wasnidge's hardware store.

Meanwhile four of Joseph's brothers, William, Thomas, Samuel, and Alexander were all attracted to the hardware business, at that time one of the most lucrative lines of work in Montreal, so Joseph had many people he could consult. These companies imported from the States high quality iron tools, such as agricultural implements and axes. In 1830 William joined the firm of John Frothingham, another Unitarian friend, who at that time managed one of the largest wholesale firms in British North America. He became a full partner in 1834.

Thomas, until then serving an apprenticeship elsewhere, promptly joined Frothingham and Workman as a junior clerk. Even Alexander, when he moved to Bytown (later known as Ottawa), started up a hardware business there with another Unitarian, Edward Griffin. So again Joseph was following in his brothers' footsteps rather than developing his own unique career, albeit in a different city.

The Workman parents remained in the Montreal area, moving up river to New Glasgow near Lachine, to be of support to their son John's widow and her new baby, named Margaret after Ben's wife. They were also afraid of the cholera so rampant in the ports. They lived there for several years until John's widow remarried. Joseph Workman, Senior, died, aged eighty-nine, on September 13, 1848, and Catharine moved back to Montreal, living next door to her son Samuel and his family, after he had returned from assisting Joseph in Toronto.[10]

In 1839 another loss had hit the Workman family. The youngest son, Matthew Francis, had arrived in Canada when only a boy of twelve, and had probably attended the Union School as a non-paying student. He too would have left his mark on Canadian society if he had not become stricken with tuberculosis in May of 1839. He showed academic brilliance as indicated in the records of the Natural History Society of Montreal. Two years before his death, when he was twenty-two years old, he was awarded their Silver Prize Medal for his essay "On the connection between the language and character of a people." The judges commented on his "great powers of analysis and comparison on a subject of an abstract nature, worthy of an advanced scholar with acute intellectual powers." The *Montreal Gazette* wrote a glowing obituary suggesting that the disease was brought on by an "overstrained application to study, the result of a too fervent thirst after knowledge."[11] Matthew Francis's interest in the origins of words seems an echo of Joseph's fascination with language and its sources. Presumably they gained this interest from a common source, probably their father, who was reputed to love the art of conversation.

When Joseph left Montreal and moved to Toronto, it was the first time in his life that he was not surrounded by one or more of his siblings. It was like a second emigration. Transportation was still relatively slow and difficult, discouraging frequent trips back and forth. Joseph did make efforts to keep in close touch, mostly by letters. Of all the brothers, Joseph wrote most fondly of Thomas. Occasionally Thomas visited him in Toronto, and Joseph certainly made trips to Montreal whenever his responsibilities allowed.

His brother Samuel came to Toronto for a few years in the mid 1840s to help him with the hardware business, but there did not seem to be a close bond between the two. It was more a case of expediency. Many years passed before Benjamin joined Joseph in what was to become his life's work in Toronto. Joseph had influenced Ben to enter medicine in 1850, and he admired and trusted Ben. When he needed a reliable assistant in 1856, he invited Ben to join him at the Asylum. Ben also admired Joseph and was humble enough to accept direction from his younger brother when the time came. He was able to work under Joseph for nineteen years.

Although he never returned to live in Montreal, Joseph did not lose touch with his family, nor with several of the new friends he had made during his seven years there. But in essence he was entering a new phase of his life when he left the city for Toronto.

CHAPTER FOUR

Pioneer Days in Toronto
(1836-1853)

*"The first step in any educational process is to inculcate in the
mind of youth the great principles of honesty, truth,
benevolence, loyalty to just authority and
withstanding of tyranny and
oppression of any sort."*
J.W.

EXTENDED family responsibilities brought Joseph Workman to Toronto, but the life of the town made him stay. From comments he
made, it is clear that he enjoyed being in at the beginning of things,
whether that be a town rapidly expanding, a school system just opening up or a new asylum about to be built. Toronto reflected the great
societal changes going on in Canada, with the breakdown of the old
rural, hierarchical communities, and the development of an urban,
industrial, more democratic society. Joseph saw himself as a pioneer
and enjoyed questioning oppressive mores and institutions, as suggested by the quotation given above. The next period of his life illustrates this well, particularly the era from 1845 to 1853 during which
he was involved in the establishment of several important public and
democratic institutions in Toronto. Indeed his whole life in Toronto
speaks to this characteristic! In a letter to a colleague he articulated
this interest: "The beginning of any good work is its most valuable
part."[1]

Joseph came to Toronto for a five week visit in 1836 to survey
the situation. He liked what he saw. Toronto, with a population of
9,254 people, officially had become a city two years before. Com-

pared to Montreal, however, it was still a pioneering community, or, as one traveller commented, "a stagnant backwater." The sidewalks were made of wood, the streets were muddy, and there was no sewage system or street lighting. The core of the town was on the west bank of the Don, surrounded still by woods, fields and marshy areas. The population was mostly white, Anglo-Saxon Protestant, dominated by the Anglican Church and the English aristocratic families, known as the Family Compact. Toronto was situated in Upper Canada, which became Canada West in 1840 and Ontario in 1867. There was rapid development in the years following 1834, and by 1841 the population was 40,000.

William Lyon Mackenzie was elected the first Mayor of Toronto in 1834, and led the Rebellion of 1837 against the forces of the Family Compact. There is no record of Joseph's thoughts or involvement during this period, although he later had some contact with Mackenzie. He did become close friends with a Dr. John Rolph, who had participated in the Rebellion and who was a well-known leader in the Liberal Reform movement. Joseph certainly supported democratic reform but he was cautious at that time and very new to the city. Most of his energies were going into his business and his new young family. In addition, he had taken on some extra responsibility for his wife's family.

While he was helping his mother-in-law run the Wasnidge hardware store, his medical skills had to be placed on hold, not to be picked up again until ten years had passed. He already knew a little about the hardware business, because it was the line of work chosen by several of his brothers. He knew that the opportunities were expanding as demand was growing rapidly for quality household and farming tools. He took on the job mainly out of a sense of duty, but part of him was genuinely interested in trying his hand at the business. It was unfortunate, however, that (according to family records) the younger Wasnidge sons, still adolescents in 1836, resented Joseph's presence and felt he usurped their family business. So in 1840 Joseph started his own store under the name of the Workman Brothers Hardware.[2] He persuaded his brother, Samuel, to come from Montreal to help him run the business which freed him for other interests. His store was situated at 36 King Street East, opposite St. James's Anglican Cathedral.

At that time young Alfred Wasnidge took over the management of the Wasnidge Ironmongers store, situated at 101 King St. East. Then several more tragedies struck. Elizabeth's mother died in 1843. Her brother Henry, who was assisting Alfred, died in 1845. Alfred also died young, as did her other brother, Joseph, who had taken up farming. Her sister died in childbirth, leaving Elizabeth, in 1861, as the only Wasnidge left from the eight who had emigrated in 1829. Despite the unpredictability of life in those times, such severe losses were unusual. (See Chapter Fourteen for further details.)

From 1845 on, Joseph seemed to be freed up enough from his business demands to take on several community roles. By this time he was forty years old and financially relatively well established. In 1845 Joseph's name appears as one of the founders of the Board of Trade, and he served on their first Executive.[3] Following his resignation on October 2, 1846, the president, George Ridout (another hardware merchant) and the rest of the Board gave him a unique gold medal as a memento. George Ridout was a staunch Conservative but much appreciated Joseph as his vice-president, despite Joseph's affiliations with the Liberal Reform party. In his farewell speech, he mentioned with affection Joseph's good sense and moderation. His colleagues on the Board were also appreciative. Joseph had explained to them the new reciprocal trade regulations, and in gratitude they reported: "The Doctor is in advance of every man in Western Canada. He has removed the mystifications by which time and cunning had surrounded the questions of Free Trade, Differential Duties, Navigation Laws, et cetera. He was first in the field. He has more sound practical knowledge of commercial questions than all of the Cabinet put together."[4] His days at the Board of

Trade were only the beginning of his role as an advocate and catalyst in the founding of new organisations.

Joseph was also the key founder of the Unitarian Congregation in Toronto in 1845, and he spent much time and energy in getting that institution established. (His important role there is the focus of Chapter Six.)

Finally in 1846 he managed to return to his chosen profession. Back in 1837 he had obtained his licence to practise medicine in Upper Canada, hoping one day to be able to use it. He had kept up his reading on the subject. He opened his own medical office in Toronto, focusing on family practice. His records, carefully preserved, show that he did not charge poor families or widows. He even saw patients on a Sunday, although the number of patients was fewer, 16 a day as compared to 29.[5] The next year he extended his work to include lectures on Midwifery, Diseases of Women and Children, and later Materia Medica. It was Dr. John Rolph, mentioned earlier, who persuaded Joseph to teach these subjects in Rolph's private medical school. Dr. Rolph had actually invited Joseph several years prior to 1847 but Joseph thought it incongruous to teach medicine while still managing a hardware store.

Dr. Rolph was an English doctor-lawyer, who had previously been a respected and articulate Member of the Assembly, and the leader of the Liberal Reformers in the 1820s in Upper Canada. Following his involvement with William Lyon Mackenzie and the Rebellion of 1837, he had thought it prudent to escape to the U.S.A. He returned in 1838, and in 1843 he set up the Rolph Medical School at the southwest corner of Yonge and Queen. Much of the accommodation was provided by a barn on the property next to his home. Dr. Geikie, one of the thirty-one students who attended, later commented that during lectures they could hear the cow and horse munching. He and the well-known writer and teacher, Dr. William Canniff, were two of Joseph's admiring students and reported enthusiastically on Joseph's popularity and ability, stating that he was an excellent speaker and teacher.[6] In 1851 this school became known as the Toronto School of Medicine. There were many problems over certification of the graduates. Joseph took a stand on behalf of the medical school but ran into serious conflict with Dr. Christopher Widmer, the wealthy and conservative Chairman of the Medical Board of Upper Canada and leader of the medical establishment. In 1851 Joseph wrote: "The school is as yet in fair repute but next winter we will see it in a lower state. There is a time for dying in both physical and public life and my belief is that it is wise to leave the stage while our fame is yet fresh."[7] The conflict was finally resolved at a medical meeting in October, 1852, at which "Dr. Widmer advanced to Dr. Workman and requested Dr. Workman to shake hands with him."[8] This act symbolised that some of the difficulties had been smoothed out. The next year, the Toronto School of Medicine became affiliated with Victoria College in Cobourg. It was eventually integrated with the Toronto Medical Faculty.

Several of Joseph's lectures have been preserved for posterity and they contain much practical advice on handling patients, as well as medical information. He brought in controversial subjects such as evolution, attempting to stimulate and entertain as well as educate. One issue of general interest was his basic belief in the value of fresh air, exercise and good food. In his view, a healthy lifestyle was the best cure for mild problems of constipation, and for "incipient menstruation" in young adolescent girls, a condition which seemed to bother their conscientious mothers.[9] He suggested that, unfortunately, such advice would not make physicians wealthy, for those desiring wealth would advocate medicines, bleeding, purging and the dark room. He was particularly concerned at the high mortality rates for infants in North America compared with Great Britain. Since he had lost four of his own children, this was also a personal concern. One of his children died of "lung problems," and another (ten-month old Alfred) died of "dysentery during teething."[10]

Joseph did have a little spare time, however, during his early years in Toronto, to develop one of his useful political tools, the power of the pen. During the late 1830s he began to write letters, articles and editorials. He became for a time a chief editorial writer of one of the Reform movement newspapers, the *Mirror*, later called the *Toronto Mirror*, which had been founded by two Irish Catholics in 1837. (Joseph also placed his business ads in the *Mirror*.) There are suggestions that he may have written occasionally for Francis Hincks's *Examiner*, another Liberal Reformist newspaper, and later on for the *Leader*, although the latter did not start until 1852. He had a witty, sarcastic and often ironic style of writing which his admirers liked, believing that he mixed high ideals with basic common sense, but his political foes were very critical. One opponent commented: "When editor of a Roman Catholic paper, the *Toronto Mirror*, he was looked upon as the most bitter and reckless slanderer that ever handled a pen; perfectly unscrupulous, but far too practised and wary a controversialist to make a direct charge when an insinuation would answer his purpose."[11] This was the first time Joseph publicly displayed the provocative and controversial aspect of his personality. Nevertheless, he seemed to remain generally popular and was elected to public office in 1847.

Joseph's interest in politics, and especially local community issues, led him to run for the position of alderman for Saint David's Ward from 1847 to 1849. As alderman, he was chosen to serve on the Board of Health, the Education Committee, and on the Standing Committee of Finance and Assessment. In the latter committee he was interested in freeing voting from vested interests, in a Bill called the Freedom of Elections. This was an important step in promoting democratic principles in local government. The Education Committee was concerned with establishing a public school system. Because of the lack of public financing, there was little money to pay teachers and build adequate schools, so Joseph took on the role of advocating for the payment of these educational expenses or debts.[12] The situation was not fully resolved until 1850 when the first Board of Education was elected. Joseph again participated in the founding of a key public institution, this time the Toronto public school system. (This story is recounted in the next chapter.)

The third committee on which Joseph served was that of Health. In keeping with his earlier interest in cholera, Joseph encouraged the Board of Health (which he chaired) to set up the Emigrant Hospital, and together with the Toronto General Hospital, they tried to help sick and destitute immigrants. In 1847 a large number of Irish had arrived, escaping from the failed potato harvests. It was a concern close to Joseph's heart. Even larger numbers were expected in 1848 and 1849, so in 1847 Joseph wrote to the Governor General in Montreal seeking financial help for provisions, medicine and medical assistance, which was immediately granted.[13] In an eleven month period 4,772 immigrants were assisted. Nevertheless, 881 died, but mostly from malnutrition and other diseases, and relatively few from the very contagious Asiatic Cholera, which was the major concern.[14] They avoided a major epidemic. It was during this period that Joseph first met the well-known Dr. Chrisopher Widmer, who was at that time the Chairman of the Toronto General Hospital, and on this occasion he found him very helpful. Together they set up the Emigrant Hospital.

On July 9, 1849, Joseph suddenly resigned from his role as alderman. This may have been connected with the death of his second daughter, Catharine, aged seventeen months. A more likely reason, however, was probably the carry-over from his appointment in 1848 to the Royal Commission to investigate the finances of King's College and Upper Canada College. This had become an arduous and very important job for the three men appointed. Although originally scheduled for only three months, it extended right into 1850, and parts of it even into 1852.[15] Joseph had become the key author of the Report. The controversy had been ongoing for some time. In 1827 a very large area of land in the city (225,944 acres of Crown Land) had been placed under the control of the Episcopal or Anglican Church, by means of a charter obtained by Bishop Strachan in 1826 for the purposes of creating a University. Bishop Strachan believed in expanding the training of Anglican clergy for it was evident to him that "infidel and democratic principles are in unison and are spreading far and wide" so "it is of the greatest importance that the education of the Colony should be conducted by the clergy."[16] In 1831 Upper Canada College school had opened and in 1843 King's College University. Both were tightly controlled by the Anglican hierarchy. Three small colleges of other denominations had opened close by, but received no great financial support. The new Canadian Reform Party government of Lafontaine and Robert Baldwin had wanted to open up the opportunity for university education ever since they had first gained power in 1841. They had been frustrated in their earlier attempts, but after they were re-elected in 1848, they appointed a Royal Commission to explore what was happening to the income from the vast Clergy Reserve Lands. The Royal Commission Reports documented gross mismanagement, with large sums of money unaccounted for (a hundred and sixty six thousand pounds) and expenditures exceeding recorded revenue. Joseph noted that there was about three thousand pounds owing to the government in rent arrears which had been collected already by the Bursar of the Clergy Reserve Lands, and he lamented that this could have been spent for roads and bridges, or for the deaf and dumb. Joseph also had to struggle and complain before he and the clerks were paid for their expenses in writing the Report. In the interim Joseph even had to borrow money from one of his brothers to pay his own debts (obligations on behalf of his family and the Unitarian Congregation), but he felt that the pecuniary sacrifice was worth it, just to finish the task properly. He made three hundred and thirteen personal visits to collect information, and worked many hours at home, going far beyond the call of duty, persevering despite the deliberate obstructions put in his path by those he was investigating. Even before the results were officially presented, the government took action. King's College was closed in 1849 and University College was built (1856 to 1859). One of Joseph's fellow Commissioners, Judge Robert Burns, was appointed Chancellor of the new University in 1857. Non-sectarian, universal, university education began in Toronto. The College became a model for the British Empire,[17] and Joseph had once again been involved in laying the foundations of a new institution. His understanding of responsible business practices, his liking for detective work, and his skill in writing had been put to good political use for a cause in which he ardently believed. The Provincial Secretary even put forward a recommendation to the Lieutenant Governor that a statue to Joseph be erected on the University College grounds, but no one listened!

CHAPTER FIVE

The Struggle for Free Public Schooling
(1847-1854)

"Learning is the greatest gift you can give a child and benefits society by diminishing crime ... If we educate the next generation properly, they may be able to solve for us all the problems we only compound each time we approach them."
J.W.

As mentioned earlier, there was a struggle over basic elementary schooling at the same time as the battle over university education was going on. Egerton Ryerson, as the Superintendent of Education for Canada West (later called Ontario), had been promoting progressive ideas at the provincial level, but then it was up to municipalities to implement his recommendations. In 1847, when Joseph was an alderman sitting on the Education Committee, the municipality had nominated three men to sit on what was called a Board of School Trustees, but Joseph was not one of them. They were chosen to represent the principal religious denominations, and were relatively progressive thinkers who favoured free education. The bill to collect the necessary money for the public schools, however, had not been included in the legislation, so little materialised until 1850 when Ryerson's third School Act was passed. On October 23, 1850, the first election for the Board of Education took place. At that time it was given full powers to manage the schools and the right to collect its own taxes, a very controversial issue. Joseph not only was elected but was chosen by his colleagues (one of whom was George Ridout of the Board of Trade) to be the first Chairman. He was reelected the two subsequent years.

The issues at stake at that first election are well documented. For example, there was much debate whether or not to charge fees. In 1850 there were over a thousand students in private schools, and about the same number in public schools, but the majority of children (over three thousand) were not in any school at all and had nothing constructive with which to fill their time. There was concern about the possibility of these children getting involved in crime, and it was argued that if schools were free and most children attended, crime would diminish. (Compulsory education was still some time down the road.) Back in 1836 Dr. Charles Duncombe wrote a poignant description of Toronto's street children: "Every person that frequents the streets of this City must be forcibly struck with the ragged and uncleanly appearance, the vile language, the idle and miserable habits of numbers of children, most of whom are of an age suitable for schools or for some useful employment. The parents of these children, are, in all probability, too poor, or too degenerate, to provide them with clothing fit for them to be seen in at school; and know not where to place them in order that they may find employment. What can be expected, but that such children will in due time, become responsible to the laws of crimes which have thus, in a manner, been forced upon them."[1] Joseph himself said "Learning is the greatest gift you can give a child and benefits society by diminishing crime." Many of the Toronto children were increasingly poor Irish immigrants, who reminded Joseph of the conditions in his homeland and why he himself had emigrated.

A group of citizens, however, became extremely agitated at such thinking and petitioned the Mayor, John G. Bowes, protesting against free schooling. A big public meeting was held on January 6, 1852, with about four hundred citizens in attendance. One criticism raised was that Toronto was introducing "communism in education" and encouraging the "undermining of property and society."[2] Joseph used wit and sarcasm to demolish the arguments of the opponents of free education. The chief antagonist was one Angus Dallas, who claimed that the Massachusetts Board of Education had reported unfavourably regarding free schools. Joseph made fun of his comments, suggesting that Canada West had wasted its money sending Dr. Egerton Ryerson abroad to Europe and the U.S.A. to report on the issue, when Angus Dallas could all the while have given the report himself. Egerton Ryerson, also a renowned orator, spoke after Joseph. Mr. Dallas could not stand up to their combined eloquence, and several prominent citizens changed sides, the most noteworthy being the Honorable Henry John Boulton, a former Attorney-General for Upper Canada. Joseph summed up the debate by commenting that the wealthy did not want to spend their money assisting the children of the poorer classes; and they complained because "their pockets were never touched before."[3] Money was needed not only for the teachers' salaries but to upgrade the existing school buildings which were very unhealthy and inadequate structures.

Another issue was how best to teach moral and religious principles. Joseph argued strongly for "no inculcation of sectarian dogma." While he accepted the fact that the Constitution gave the right to Roman Catholics to establish Separate schools, he saw this policy as creating friction by promoting social segregation in society. He observed that employment and jobs would also be affected. He summed up his thoughts by stating that it would "ultimately be detrimental to the best interests of the Roman Catholics." His preference was for various clergy to visit the schools, with all or just some of the students attending these sessions. He certainly favoured Christian teaching in the schools, stating that "education unconnected with or uncontrolled by religion, is a very unstable sort of national morality." Teachers, however, should "refrain from public, political and ecclesiastical controversy."[4] True to his Unitarian beliefs, Joseph did not favour the recitation of the Lord's Prayer in school, but after he left the Board in 1854, the Lord's Prayer was introduced at the beginning and end of each school day, along with a reading from the Old and New Testaments respectively.[5] The official documents stated simply that good manners, morals, and cleanliness would be taught, along side discipline "such as would be exercised by a kind and judicious parent."

Another of Joseph's beliefs was that the great emphasis on the prize system was detrimental to learning. In his personal diary he wrote that it was "calculated mainly to gratify the vanity of a very few who might advance very well without it."[6] He also wrote a lengthy article describing how it discouraged those who did not receive any prizes from believing in themselves or developing independent thinking, which he saw as a tragedy.

He described the goals of education: "The first step in any educational process is to inculcate in the mind of youth the great principles of honesty, truth, benevolence, loyalty to just authority and withstanding of tyranny and oppression of any sort. Next is to be placed the acquirement of that knowledge necessary to our immediate comforts and interests; and after that, accomplishments and refinements; in their proper order of succession, the good, the useful, and the ornamental."[7]

The above principles were those of the Workman family. All the brothers had been instilled with a strong sense of morality, had learned skills to earn their living, possessed an ability to think through issues for themselves, and seemed to seek knowledge for its own sake. Refinements such as art, music, and the theatre took low priority. Joseph himself epitomised this philosophy. Sometimes he became discouraged about the school system. At other times he wrote "If we educate the next generation properly, they may be able to solve for us all the problems we only compound each time we approach them." In addition he was concerned about the lack of responsibility shown by many businessmen and corporations towards the community, "men who find no qualms of conscience in pocketing the increased profits of business. In trade as in war, every stratagem is legitimate. These men may be clever merchants, but they are badly educated men. They may be gathering gold; but they are dropping diamonds while picking it up."[8]

Joseph's attitude to the role of women (also displayed in the Unitarian Congregation's constitution of 1845) is elaborated upon in that same article. "There can be no reason why a young woman should not receive an extended and refined education; and nothing appears to me to savour more of barbarism than the notion that women should be excluded from the study of the more profound branches of literature and science. No surer proof can be afforded of the advancement of natural refinement, than the fact that the rights of women are respected, and their full equality to us, in both moral and mental power, is recognized." However, he goes on to add: "She may study geology, but she should not be ignorant of the structure of a plum pudding; she may receive lessons on the piano, but not to the exclusion of her studies on the darning needle, or the smoothing iron."[9] The Toronto schools prided themselves on separating the girls' classes from those of the boys. Decorum as well as separate subject matter was the reasoning. For several decades, however, and in both streams, the quality of education was of a very low standard, and it took time for this to rise.

At the beginning of Joseph's third term of office on January 21, 1852, he gave an impressive and lengthy inaugural address, in which he thanked his colleagues for their support in this "intellectual reformation."[10] But two months later he resigned from the chairmanship, although he continued to be active for over two more years.[11] No reason was given in his letter of resignation. At that time he seemed fairly busy completing the Royal Commission expense sheets and extra reports, but some additional unknown factor may have occurred that he did not want made public.

Joseph never returned to active involvement in the school system. In retirement, however, he gave a keynote address to the Provincial Teachers Association, his topic being "Morbid Results of

Persistent Mental Overwork."[12] He commented that the audience was large and appreciative, but he did not elaborate on whether he was talking about the students' or the teachers' overwork, or both! Another contact came in 1881 when Joseph was elected the first President of the Ontario Medical Association. A motion was passed at that founding meeting to advocate "the teaching of hygiene to all pupils in the public schools as a means of preventing sickness and promoting well-being."

Joseph's varied public activities in Toronto came to a gradual close in 1853. But he did not withdraw totally from all his commitments until the following year when his appointment at the Asylum was made permanent. For example, he did not resign from the Board of Education until the end of 1854. His new job at the Asylum was, however, very demanding, and gave him little time for other responsibilities.

In analyzing Joseph's life during these early years in Toronto, it is remarkable that he could be involved in so many varied and demanding activities. He never complained of mental overwork. It has been reported that he could cope with very little sleep, and that he had an amazing memory. He appears to be what has been described as a "Renaissance man", an achiever in many different fields of endeavour. He certainly loved to read, and his reading ranged over a wide variety of topics, but none frivolous! He also spoke and read in ten different languages. No wonder he was highly respected and much admired. He had relatively few real enemies despite his outspokenness and often sarcastic humour. George Brown, founder of the *Globe*, seemed to be his most important and most vocal critic. (See Chapter Seven.) A few other critics are recorded from time to time, and Joseph himself writes about them, often feeling indignant over what he considered unjustified criticism. He prided himself on his loyalty to his friends, and in turn he seemed to inspire loyalty as well as admiration.

CHAPTER SIX

Founding the Unitarian Congregation (1845-1854)

"The church has ever been among the objects dearest to my heart; and as long as God spares me life and health I trust never to forsake it, in whatsoever trial."

J.W.

JOSEPH was the key founder of the First Unitarian Congregation of Toronto in 1845. Prior to this date, Unitarians had been meeting in private homes. Joseph had close ties to his brothers in the Montreal congregation and so learned that their new Irish minister, the Rev. John Cordner, was interested in visiting Toronto to see if there was enough public response to start a Toronto church. As Cordner had been chosen by Joseph's minister in Ireland, the Rev. Henry Montgomery, Joseph felt a personal connection to Cordner. (See Chapter Two.) On July 6 Cordner preached in Toronto, and the turnout was encouraging. As a result, on July 9, 1845, fifteen families met to establish the congregation, with Joseph as the first lay preacher. Within a few weeks they found their first minister, the Rev. William Adam, but unfortunately he only remained one year, and for the next four years the small group struggled on without a minister.

For nearly ten years, on and off, Joseph served on the Board of Trustees. Most of the other members were independent businessmen, who looked up to Joseph, the most educated and the obvious leader. Despite this, Joseph insisted on being the Secretary, not the Chairman of the Board of Trustees. His stamp is clearly seen in the writing of the constitution of the congregation and in the long range planning.[1] The religious principles and practices were not unlike those of his church in Ulster. Although they described themselves as a Christian Society, one of the key tenets was "the free exercise of private judgment in all matters of belief and the rejection of all tests, creeds or formal declarations of opinion." Another clause stated that "females ... were to attend all meetings of the congregation and to exercise the same privileges as members of this society as are exercised by males."[2] This was certainly progressive thinking for 1845.

Joseph was also involved in the purchase of the small chapel at 113 George Street in 1845, and in the planning for a larger church building at 216 Jarvis Street seven years later. Strangely enough, the Unitarians sold their chapel to the newly formed Cooke's Presbyterians, several of whom had emigrated from the north of Ireland. (Old world loyalties took on a different meaning in the new land!) Donations were sought for the new church, and Joseph's name headed the list with a donation of $200. Another Irish Unitarian family was also represented, with Professor William Hincks, the brother of Francis, being a key contributor. Francis, now a Member of Parliament, also began to attend the Toronto congregation when the Canadian parliament moved from Montreal to Toronto. He donated for the new minister in 1850, but his name was not on the donation list in 1852 for the building of the new church.[3]

An undeveloped lot on Jarvis Street was purchased by four members but registered in Joseph's name. It is not certain whether this was for legal reasons, financial purposes or because the conservative Torontonians did not want to sell to the "heretical" Unitarians. When the congregation had difficulty collecting enough money to pay for the whole lot, Joseph bought the western section in 1855 for his own personal use, eventually building his own house on this land, at 113 Mutual Street, and renting out the two terrace houses which he had built on the adjacent lots.

In 1853 there was a major fight within the congregation regarding the financing of the new Gothic structure on Jarvis Street. The minister at the time, Rev. Charles Dall, had travelled extensively in the U.S.A. to solicit funds and he had promised that there would be no mortgage on the building. But Joseph and the Board had hired one of the most prominent architects of the day, William Thomas, who also designed the St. Lawrence Hall, St. Michael's Cathedral and what is now known as Oakham House. They were reluctant to cut back their plans when the expenses started to rise above the estimates. A strike by the builders exacerbated the situation. Joseph insisted that the congregation hold a mortgage, but the minister was equally adamant that there be no mortgage. Feelings ran high, and finally the minister had an emotional breakdown and resigned. Joseph, as usual, won the day, but there was considerable empathy for the minister and his efforts. Joseph asked to have the negative exchange of letters expunged from the records of the Board of Trustees, and complained to his colleagues on the Board of Trustees of the "unmerited indignity" he underwent. (See the Appendix for the sequence of events and the powerful letters written by Joseph to the minister and the Board of Trustees.)[4]

Benjamin's fight over ministerial power in the Montreal congregation in 1855-56 concerned a similar issue (described in the Appendix, under Ben's Story). Based on the principle of democratic decision-making within the congregation, both brothers were resistant to the minister making important decisions, especially financial ones, on behalf of the congregation. Added to this debate was the confrontation of strong personalities.

In 1966 a key article written about Joseph stated that he was only briefly involved with the Unitarians, and that he helped found the group only because he wanted to establish a free-thinking group.[5] Presumably the writer was unaware that Joseph was raised in the liberal Non-Subscribing Presbyterian Church (see Chapter Two), which was and still is in association with the Unitarians. Throughout his life Joseph never appeared to stray far from Unitarian principles and ideas. The author of the article was responding to the entry in Joseph's diary for November 21, 1869, which stated that a writer in writer in the *Globe* had charged him with the "crime of being a Unitarian, and not feeling very sure as to the truth of this charge, I attended the Unitarian Church for the first time for a number of years, as it seemed to me a duty to reduce the charge as far as possible from falsehood." Interestingly the event seemed to revive a former interest in theology for that same month his diary records that he read *The Christ of History, Rationalism in Europe*, and the works of Channing, a famous Unitarian.

There are four main explanations of Joseph's lack of involvement in the life of the congregation from 1854 (when he resigned as a Trustee of the Congregation) until the 1870s. First, he had very little free time. It was said he usually worked about eighty to ninety hours a week, and often isolated himself for months on end at the Asylum. On top of that he had family obligations. Second, it was a relatively long distance to the church at 216 Jarvis Street from the Asylum at 999 Queen Street West. Third, while the Unitarians believe in regular church attendance, it is not obligatory. The last and perhaps the most important reason of all, is that Ben had a need to take Joseph's place within the congregation. The two brothers were working together all day, and the opinionated Ben would surely need a place where his younger brother was not the leader. Joseph had the wisdom to recognize this.

After the first intensive involvement from 1845 to 1854, Joseph did keep up some contacts with the Unitarians. In 1856 he hired Mary Anna Parkes, a church member, to be the Asylum matron and she remained for the next twenty years. His diary noted the invitation to the Unitarian Dramatic Club to perform at the Asylum, and also his attendance at the funeral of Professor William Hincks, along with Ben, on September 18, 1871. All six of Joseph's surviving children were baptized by a Unitarian minister.

One touching event is recorded at one of the baptisms. Since Toronto frequently did not have a fulltime minister, it was not inappropriate for the Irish minister from Montreal, John Cordner, to visit. On one such occasion on September 27, 1862, Joseph invited him to baptize Thomas, aged 9, Florence, aged 11, and his 6 year old niece, Elizabeth Wasnidge, known as Lizzie. The christening was a private ceremony at the Workman apartments at the Asylum. An unmarried mother, named Susan Potcher, also had her baby christened at the same event, and Mary Parkes was the sponsor or god-parent. This was an unusual event, even amongst the liberal Unitarians.

Joseph also kept up some of his former friendships, such as those with Thomas Burgess (Senior), and with Peter Lamb and his son, Daniel, the alderman who founded Riverdale zoo. He corresponded on occasion with two Unitarian ministers, James Hodgins of Hamilton, and A. R. Kennedy of Toronto. And he left $150 in his will to the Congregation. One of the witnesses to his signature on the will was John Bertram, a Unitarian and a Liberal Member of the House of Commons. Finally, Joseph requested that his funeral be held in the Unitarian Church, and this was conducted by Rev. Henry Woude, the Unitarian minister at that time.

The free thinking ideas which Joseph articulated were essentially the Christian Unitarian beliefs current in the nineteenth century, whether they were against "fulminating pulpit orators," or for a more compassionate view of God's love to humankind, which Joseph described as "God's powers of pardon."[6] The innate worth of every human being was, he felt, one of the basic teachings of Jesus. He believed in and practised religious tolerance as long as the other's faith brought comfort and guidance. For example, many people he admired belonged to one of the major Christian churches, such as Catholic, Presbyterian or Anglican. He and his family often attended one of their Asylum services, and he developed friendships with several of the regular visiting clergy. In his diary a Rev. Dr. Kennedy of the Anglicans was mentioned, a Rev. Dr. Burns of the Presbyterians, as well as Father Laurent of St. Michael's and the Fathers of St. Mary's. The fact that none of the children chose to remain practising Unitarians suggests that they developed other religious ties. For example, the oldest boy, William, taught Sunday School for many years at the Unitarian church in Montreal, but when he settled in Stratford he attended the Anglican Church with his wife who had been raised in that denomination. It is doubtful, however, if Joseph himself would have called himself other than a Non-Subscribing Presbyterian or a Unitarian.

After Joseph withdrew from active leadership in the congregation in 1854, his brother Benjamin in 1856 moved in to fill his place. His heartbreaks in Montreal have already been touched on. He had lost two wives, a son, and the congregation he had helped build. He did receive, however, a very large and beautiful Bible from the Montreal Sunday School as a thank you present, a gift that he later bequeathed to Joseph. But it was a lonely and sad man who arrived in Toronto in 1856. Luckily he found a ready welcome at the Unitarian Congregation, augmented by the fact that they had just lost their minister, Charles Dall, as well as Joseph, their previous leader, who was now totally immersed in his new job at the Asylum. Professor William Hincks had agreed to be the unpaid minister, a role he performed for four years. (He had had theological training and experience in the old country before emigrating.)[7] The Sunday School and the other pastoral duties, however, needed a leader, and Ben jumped in with both feet. The congregation became his family. He served on the Board, and for one year (1869) was elected Chairman or President. He ran the Sunday School for nine years as well as leading the Sunday Services for two years, during another period without a hired minister. He even conducted a funeral. As with Professor Hincks it was a labour of love. Since he had once pondered the ministry as a career, this was an opportunity to play the role, and he seemed to do it well. He was well loved in return. In gratitude the congregation gave him an exquisite silver writing desk, and his portrait was hung in a place of honour.[8]

Thus for a period of thirty years these two brothers played a key leadership role in the history of the Toronto congregation, beginning with its founding in 1845. Their contributions have not been forgotten. The largest church hall is called Workman Hall (after both brothers) and the Annual Workman Lecture is held in Joseph's honour.

The Establishment of the Asylum, and a Decade of Controversy and Scandal (1853-1860)

"Unvarying kindness, never-tiring forbearance, and undeviating truthfulness, are the cardinal moral agencies now employed in every well-conducted Lunatic Asylum; and surely no remedies could be found less expensive, or more easy of appliance."
J.W.

A PRESTIGIOUS political patronage job for Joseph! He was appointed the interim Superintendent of the Provincial Lunatic Asylum in Toronto on July 1, 1853, and the permanent Superintendent a year later. It might have been a thank-you for his commitment on the Royal Commission, or because of his connections with Dr. John Rolph and Sir Francis Hincks, or because he had the best qualifications regarding experience and personality, or a mixture of all of these.

The 1830s and 1840s were turbulent ones in the treatment of insanity. Previous to that date the insane were contained in their local communities, the quiet people often being kept in closets, cages, sheds and barns, while the acting-out ones were locked up in the jails. The eighteenth century view, that such people were possessed by demons and influenced by witchcraft, was gradually disappearing, and expressions of sympathy and concern were being recorded. The term "lunacy" was still used, however, a word suggesting that insanity is related to the influence of the moon, particularly the full moon. A new term, "alienism" was now introduced, meaning that insane patients seemed strange and alienated from this world.

The early nineteenth century was a period of rapid change. The wealthy and aristocratic classes, called the "Family Compact," were losing their power; there was growing urbanization and industrialization, and a rapid increase in immigration, especially of poverty-stricken Irish. People were beginning to wonder if there were better ways of doing things than had been done in the past. New ideas were permeating from Europe concerning treatment centres for the insane. Some modern critics have suggested that the building of asylums was motivated by middle-class groups wanting to hide the rejects of society, among whom were the insane. Placing the latter in such institutions brought order and respectability to the community. Nevertheless, the majority of citizens seemed to have more altruistic, compassionate objectives. They truly believed that 90% of the patients would be cured in the new experimental asylums being discussed.[1]

In 1830 the first Act in Upper Canada for the relief of the destitute was to legalize payment for their care in the county jail. The next year the Legislature approved the idea of an asylum, and finally, in 1835, sent Dr. Charles Duncombe on a fact-finding tour of the U.S.A. In 1841 the old jail at King and Toronto Street, described as "unfit for felons," was opened as the Provincial Lunatic Asylum! It was filled with seventeen patients who previously had been chained to the wall in the basement. In 1846 it was expanded to include the east wing of the old Upper Canada Parliament building on Front Street near Simcoe Street, unused since the Union of 1841. (Upper Canada became jointly governed with Lower Canada and was now called Canada West.) In 1844 the government bought a hundred and fifty acres of land at 999 Queen Street West. Building began two years later, but was still incomplete in 1850 when two hundred and eleven patients were placed there. This move was made necessary because rioting citizens, upset over an unpopular bill (the Rebellion

Losses Bill), had burned the current Parliament building in Montreal, forcing the quick restoration to its former use of the old Parliament building in Toronto.

Much has been written about the new Asylum building at 999 Queen Street West. The well-known architect and City Surveyor, John George Howard, drew up the plans after a careful study of several American institutions, paying particular attention to that of Worcester, Massachusetts, which had been favoured by Dr. Charles Duncombe ten years before. The new building became the third largest in North America and the largest in Canada. Its classical dome and wings were imposing and intimidating, built to impress the citizens rather than the patients. The huge dome contained a twelve thousand gallon tank, making the institution the first on the continent to provide continuous hot and cold running water.[2] Gas lighting was introduced in 1855. Later, in 1870, the May 21st edition of the *Canadian Illustrated News* called it "one of the wonders of the west."

In 1841 the first Superintendent was Dr. William Rees, intelligent and able but emotionally unstable. He began the new humanitarian treatment. Previously the patients were naked, filthy, chained and poorly fed. He arranged for regular clothing, cleanliness, decent food and even local outings, such as fishing trips. Fifty-three patients recovered under these improved conditions and were discharged. Dr. Rees, however, ran into serious conflict with the Asylum Board of Commissioners, partly because his authority was shared with them and partly because they were chosen on the grounds of patronage and not for their ability. He was replaced after eighteen months by Dr. Walter Telfer, who was accused of imbibing too much and was fired. Then came Dr. George Park, who reported that he found the Asylum in a sad condition in every respect, including intoxicated staff. This report concurred with that of Dr. J. Hack Tuke, of the famous Tuke Retreat in England, who visited during Telfer's time and described it in vivid language: "It is one of the most distressing and painful places I have ever visited. The house has a terribly dark aspect within and without. There were perhaps seventy patients upon whose faces misery and starvation and suffering were indelibly impressed. The doctor pursues the exploded system of cupping, bleeding, blistering, and purging his patients, giving them only the smallest amounts of food. The foreheads and necks of the patients were nearly all scarred with the marks of former cuppings or bandaged from the effects of recent ones. Strongly built men were shrunk to skeletons."[3] Giving the patients limited amounts of food seemed to be partly parsimony but partly policy. The ill-fed patients had then no energy with which to act out, giving the impression of having improved.

There was also controversy, nevertheless, around Dr. Park because it was thought to be a purely patronage appointment. The next Superintendent, a Dr. Primrose, lasted a year, followed by Dr. John Scott, an irritable and overbearing man from Britain. Many complaints arose. On November 12, 1851, the *Examiner* newspaper reported that dead patients were being used for dissecting experiments. A coffin from the Asylum was said to have an incomplete body in it. That was nearly the end of Dr. Scott's tenure. Investigations, however, were carried out by Susanna Moodie, the well-known writer, and by two Grand Juries, who all reported positively. It was a new act regarding the Asylum that made Dr. Scott hand in his resignation. This piece of legislation, called the Act for the Better Management of the Provincial Lunatic Asylum of Toronto, contained some major changes. The positive aspect for him was that the Superintendent was now placed in charge of staffing and finances, but with limited power over the Bursar, a new position, whom he was unable to fire. His salary was set at five hundred pounds. The Board of Commissioners was replaced by Visiting Commissioners, who wielded less power than their predecessors. But Dr. Scott feared that the government would now have greater direct control of the Asylum, and he had had enough of that.

After Dr. Scott resigned in March, 1853, the government became concerned at all the friction. The debate regarding the next appointment was reflected in the press. The *Daily Leader*, on July 13, wrote: "It is notorious that imported officials, the present government excepted, have been the worst that we have ever seen in the colonies." Such sentiments favoured the appointment of a local doctor. Other factors were also at work, such as the role played by Joseph's friend, Dr. John Rolph.

Dr. Rolph, in addition to running the Toronto School of Medicine, had been selected to join his Liberal Reform colleagues in the cabinet of the new Hincks-Morin Administration. He was given the powerful position of President of the Council. Dr. Park was his brother-in-law and in the past Rolph had occasionally acted as the temporary Asylum Superintendent during Park's absences. As a result of this experience Rolph had advocated strongly that the Superintendent be able to fire "incompetents." In 1853 he nominated his protégé, Dr. Joseph Workman, to be the interim Superintendent, while a permanent appointee was being sought. The government advertised extensively, including notices in English newspapers and medical journals. Several experienced men applied. The Governor, Lord Elgin, had his own political protégé, a Dr. Robinson. Others favoured the return of Dr. Park. Joseph was also nominated for the permanent position. As mentioned, Sir Francis Hincks was then one of the joint prime ministers of the Administration. Despite his religious and political affiliations with Joseph, it is uncertain if he played any major part in the selection process. Perhaps he just left that to Dr. Rolph whom he had brought into the government. An interesting role, however, was played by the conservative Dr. Christopher Widmer, the Chairman of the Medical Board of Upper Canada, with whom Joseph had clashed in 1851 on the issue of medical exams. Since Dr. Widmer had been made the Chairman of the Board of the Asylum in 1850, his opinion was of paramount importance. By 1953 he appeared to have made his peace with Joseph, but later that year he spoke out against his nomination, stating that he was apprehensive because Joseph was a powerful presence and a political ally of Dr. Rolph. When, however, it seemed that Joseph might get the permanent job, he switched allegiance. He not only wrote a testimonial for Joseph but gave Dr. Rolph on two occasions sound political advice regarding Joseph. First, he told Dr. Rolph to advertise widely without displaying his prejudice; and then, when the names were submitted to him as President of the Council, to choose Joseph. He declared to Dr. Rolph that Joseph was very capable and he anticipated that he could do the job. Later, after Joseph had been selected, Dr. Rolph was planning to send Joseph on an educational tour of "professional observation" to Europe and the U.S.A. Again Dr. Widmer offered advice: that such a trip would indicate Joseph needed the education; was not fully prepared; and lacked practical experience; so "the shafts of political animosity will fly thickly around his ears." Why not quietly wait a year, and then let Joseph go on his tour.[4] Dr. Widmer may have genuinely changed his mind or perhaps he was politically astute and decided to make a friend of both Joseph and John Rolph.

The final selection of Joseph was not just a question of patronage. There was also much local public support.[5] Many glowing references were received, most apparently requested by Joseph himself. First, as mentioned above, came Dr. Widmer's testimonial in which he said he had "enjoyed many opportunities of observing Dr. Workman's talents and his powerful mental and bodily activity, as well as a philosophical turn for investigating the phenomena of mental disease." He added a personal letter for Joseph saying that he truly and justly believed Joseph would make an important contribution to medical knowledge.[6] In another testimonial, the Roman Catholic Bishop of Toronto admired Joseph's kindness and attentiveness to his patients. Two professors of his at McGill respected his professional skills, one calling him "first among equals." Judge Robert Burns (from his days on the Royal Commission), called him "a man of warm and benevolent and philanthropic feelings" who exhibited "no ordinary measure of judgment, decision and self-command." A clergyman also wrote a testimonial saying that he was delighted that Joseph was beginning to implement the long-awaited reforms.[7]

MacDermot in his history of the period wrote that Joseph had displayed the "tenacity of purpose in face of ignorance and prejudice" which would be needed for the job, as well as a kind and caring personality. He continued: "No one until we come to Osler commands our attention and respect to a greater degree ... (he) spent twenty-one years (actually twenty-two) turning the Asylum into a modern institution, and incidently making himself famous for his methods of dealing with the insane. He gave them a freedom which shocked his contemporaries, and did all he could to improve their surroundings. His originality and freshness of expression made him an unusually attractive personality. He contributed abundantly to the medical journals and even translated most of the work done in Italy at the time of the anatomy and physiology of the brain." He went on to add that Joseph had a "forceful and vivid style of writing, a keen sense of humour, and hated sham and pretence." MacDermot was also honest about the personality conflicts that arose, and wrote: "Like most men who are in advance of his time, and who speak their mind, he had his enemies. He was assailed in the press for his view regarding responsibility in the insane, but he was a man of vigour, of wit, and possessed of a well-sharpened and well-trained pen, and attacked quite as successfully as he resisted."[8]

During his first year in office, 1853-54, Joseph had to cope with several crises. First, there was an outbreak of typhoid at the Asylum. Joseph explored and decided it was caused by a "foul and enormous cesspool" under the basement floor, three to four feet deep in some locations, especially concentrated in the east end under the laundry and kitchens. The total area was 600 by 60 feet. There "accumulated a mass of filth and impure fluids, the stench from which, when first exposed, was so insufferable and overpowering, as instantly to sicken several of those who, including the Vis-

iting Commissioners, chanced to inhale it."[9] Rank fungus hung from
the decaying wood joists, and the flooring in the rooms above was
rotting. It had been noticed before, in January 1853, but the Board
and Grand Jury had probed it only superficially. They had not realized how serious was the problem and had done nothing about it.
The architect and the builders denied knowing exactly what caused
it, although Howard had warned the government that the site lacked
adequate gradient for good drainage.

Joseph explored the situation thoroughly. In addition to the lack
of gradient mentioned above, he noted that the problem might have
been diagnosed earlier if the water closet drains had been cleaned
out twice a year as ordered by the architect. Furthermore, the inte-
rior drains from the kitchen and laundry had "never been carried
out to the main sewer, which was at a short distance of 22 feet. The
remedy for this evil was palpable."[10] Later he reports that two exits
had been omitted, through "15 and 18 feet of clay respectively at
each end of the house."[11] Joseph had to wait until the cesspool was
frozen before removing it because it would have been dangerous
to agitate it in warm weather.

Since Howard was not only the architect but also the building
director, he was obviously implicated in the mistake. At first Joseph
thought the builders had deviated from the architect's plans. Three
independent sub-contractors had been hired! The builder of the
sewer had not communicated adequately with the builder of the
basement drains. No one would admit to being responsible. Later,
however, in 1876, Joseph wrote about the "serious blunder made
by architect" who failed to direct and coordinate all the operations.[12]
In another article Joseph also stressed that the government was to
blame for choosing an unsuitable site, that the land was too flat
and damp for a building of this magnitude. Some described it as a
black ash swamp, or quagmiral pits. The spot had been chosen because it was part of a Military Reserve, that is, for political reasons.[13] (The topic of the drains still causes controversy amongst

historians. Some think Joseph used hyperbole to dramatize the situation and to provoke Howard. Joseph, however, was not known to make up facts, much as he enjoyed rhetoric and embellishment.)

In addition, the ventilation system did not work because of poor design and the rooms were often full of smoke. The original system, Joseph wrote, was "so manifestly useless and absurd (that it was a) matter of surprise (it was) ever adopted."[14] Various major attempts were made to correct this, especially when the wings of the Asylum were completed, but none were totally successful. Despite this, it was reputed to be the best ventilated mental institution in North America up to 1900![15]

Luckily Joseph had a background in surveying and in hardware, for his first years were full of solving practical and structural problems. Another concern was that the water had to be pumped from the lake over a mile away, and the entrance to the pipe was located 100 feet from the sewage exit. Another blunder! In addition there was a need to install fire-prevention measures, always a problem in a large asylum. The final concern was that the building was surrounded by a wall, because there was some vague hope that it would provide protection if Toronto were invaded by the Americans and the Asylum made into a military fortification. However, it gave the appearance of locking in the patients.

After the drainage and ventilation systems were fixed, Joseph reported: "Perforating Dysenteries, intractable Diarrheas, and the whole Typhoid family of deadly complications ceased to perplex the Medical Staff."[16] Joseph also commented that there were a number of deaths from cholera during the previous winter. Possibly Joseph was guilty of some hyperbole. The Annual Reports from 1851 to the end of 1853 reveal only two deaths from dysentery, one from cholera, and none from typhoid. There was, however, before Joseph took over in July, a gap in the official reports for several months (February to June, 1853), so he might have been correct. An outside report supported Joseph's claim since it spoke of bouts of cholera in 1850 and 1852, with 13 dying out of 25 cases. The problem (at least as officially reported just prior to Joseph's arrival) seemed to be several mild outbreaks of dysentery. Certainly the overall issue in 1853 was the general health of the patients. Joseph commented that this was extremely poor. In later reports he boasted that skin infections (Erysipelas), dysentery, coughs and colds had been drastically diminished from 1854 on. He also moved quickly to improve the poor diet, and see that the patients had plenty of milk, bread and fresh meat.

An issue of interest to today's health practitioners is what Joseph did with the two hundred cartloads from the cesspool. Many years later he wrote in a letter that he put "the manure over the inside farm."[17] Since most of the cesspool was below the laundry and the kitchens, perhaps it contained little human excrement. The architect's plans described outside privies, pots in the bedrooms, and ten water closets in the main building, so it is not clear what happened to the human excrement. Certain questions arise: Did Joseph have any hesitancy in spreading the "manure" on the farm? Did he add anything to it first? What was grown in the inside farm? Did health problems result?

The relationship between John Howard, the architect, and Joseph is another interesting story. Howard was suffering much emotional stress long before Joseph arrived, as a result of the various building problems connected with the Asylum. These problems were added to other worries he had. Howard's doctor was Dr. Christopher Widmer, who was, as mentioned previously, the Chairman of the Visiting Commissioners until December, 1853. Howard wrote in his diary on March 29, 1853, that Widmer knew all the players well and understood that all this stress was killing him. Initially, in 1850, Widmer had applied leeches and given him opium, but by 1853 he had encouraged him to escape from it all.[18] So in the spring of 1853 Howard set sail for France and England. He returned in the Fall to hear the additional litany of complaints from Joseph.

Joseph did not attack the architect directly in his speeches, but his critical reports were available to the public. In these he described some of the engineering experiments as absurd and Howard's supervision as poor. In Howard's defence it could be said that he was one of the most experienced architects of his day and was pioneering in the field of asylum engineering. He tried things never confronted before. The problems were never fully solved. Nevertheless, he retired soon after this from his role as city surveyor. Then Joseph, surprisingly, in his 1856 report, described Howard as an excellent architect, and the site as the best in the circumstances. Was Joseph being sincere?

In 1874 Howard reappeared in Joseph's life, this time concerning his wife who was said to be delicate, physically and emotionally. In December of that year Howard unexpectedly visited the Asylum, selected a private room, signed a bond, and then approached Joseph to have his wife committed to the institution. To his surprise, Joseph refused, feeling Mrs. Howard was not insane. Howard then locked her up in their home, hiring a woman to attend to her basic needs. He said he could not tolerate her irritating behaviour and "running away."[19] No explanation was given for her behaviour, except it is known that she had developed breast cancer. Perhaps she also suffered from the beginnings of Alzheimer's or a similar disease, as well as some depression. For two years after his retirement Joseph offered consultations to her two family doctors and occasionally visited, suggesting that he had some serious concerns. Joseph might have acted just out of pity for Mrs. Howard, although it is possible that the disagreements existing between Howard and Joseph in 1853 and 1854 were forgiven twenty years later.

Another famous person to appear periodically in Joseph's life was the well-known American and Unitarian reformer, Dorothea Dix, who had helped establish the asylums in Newfoundland and Nova Scotia. She visited him while he was busy carting away the two hundred cartloads from the cesspool in the Asylum basement.

She wrote a negative report which Joseph considered unfair. Later on, however, in 1872, she visited again and thought favourably about his work. Joseph then asked her to give a pep talk to his nurses, and in a letter he called her "a good crank."[20]

When not worrying about the structure of the building, Joseph was fighting for more space per patient, because he believed they needed more room and more air than regular patients in a general hospital. Despite the prevailing theory that such institutions should not be built for more than 250 patients, the government had planned for 500. When Joseph arrived there were 373 patients, with slightly more men than women. Only two wings out of a planned four had been built because of lack of money, and the wards were over-crowded. Thus began Joseph's ongoing battle for more space. Initially everyone, including Joseph, believed that the turnover would be so high that more room would be created as patients were being cured at a rapid rate. But that was not to be the case. So Joseph argued that the overcrowding was a false economy and a great public evil, and that the success rate would be higher if the patients were not so tightly packed together. Joseph denounced the dilemma he observed in several American asylums where the Superintendent had to discharge the incurables in order to admit new patients. He added: "The community, or the Legislature, which permits such a necessity to exist, is guilty of a heinous crime against the laws of the Divine Ruler of the World, and shows a reckless disregard of the moral obligations of the Christian dispensation."

In addition, the presence of the criminally insane upset the other patients and made life very difficult for the staff. Joseph commented that it was an evil to mix "moral monsters" and also "villains who affect insanity" with gentle lunatics.[21] Thus Grace Marks, the famous alleged murderess, was sent back to Kingston Penitentiary soon after he arrived. He may not have considered her villainous, but he considered her no longer insane.[22] In 1855 Joseph did convince the government to transfer the criminally insane to Kingston, to what became the Rockwood Asylum in 1859; to relocate seventy (mostly female) patients to the University Branch in the old King's College building at Queens Park; to open in 1859 the Amherstburg Asylum in the former Fort Malden Military Barracks near Windsor; and finally, to establish Orillia in 1859, and much later, the London and Hamilton Asylums, in 1870 and 1876 respectively.

Overcrowding was always to remain a problem. The Visiting Commissioners had generally supported Joseph's pleas to complete the Toronto Asylum, but in 1857 a Board of Inspectors for Asylums and Prisons replaced them and they were less sympathetic. The completion of the Toronto Asylum was not begun until 1865 when the Secretary of State for the Colonies ordered it finished, and it was not finished till 1870. Kivas Tully was then the architect of the Public Works Department, and he modified Howard's designs somewhat. He and Joseph seemed to get along but in 1872 Tully unexpectedly criticized Joseph publicly. Joseph characteristically retaliated by complaining in his Annual Report of 1872-73 that Tully had not fixed the water closets as Joseph had requested for the past two years.[23]

At that time the Asylum was located "wholly in the country," surrounded by uncleared land, cultivated farms and gardens, and a few homes and taverns.[24] Free accommodation was provided for Joseph in the main building, spacious enough for his wife and family. (Four children were still living at home, with another, born in 1857, dying in infancy.) It seemed a healthy place to raise a family, far from the infections of the city, and during their stay the Asylum escaped any serious epidemic. It was, however, rather isolated. The staff, the patients and occasional visitors became the community. (See Chapter Ten for details.) Yet Elizabeth, Joseph's wife, seemed content. She appeared to make some new friends and took advantage of the space to indulge a hobby of hers, planting a flower garden.

Initially the grounds extended over a large area of one hundred and fifty acres of land. They were later diminished in size to only fifty acres and land was given to the Exhibition, Mercer Reformatory, various railway companies and Massey-Harris. Then in 1870 another sixty acres were added, bought from the Ordnance Department. The grounds were laid out with trees and shrubs, and, most important of all, included a farm where the male patients could learn how to grow crops and raise animals. Joseph seemed to enjoy constantly updating the grounds, as evidenced by the diagrams in his diary. He was using the skills learned while a surveyor in Ireland as well as from his days selling agricultural tools in the hardware business. He believed in occupational therapy, that is, having the male patients work in the gardens and on the farm, partly for the fresh air and exercise and partly to learn new skills, develop good habits as well as build self-esteem. The women also worked whenever possible but mostly indoors. They did traditional women's work, sewing, cooking and laundry. Quilting and embroidery were also included for the more skilled. In the early years Joseph reported that 60% of the patients were working. This was a popular idea in this era, a concept rediscovered from the past. Gardening was considered especially therapeutic. In addition many hoped it would make the Asylum more self-sufficient, and hence cut down on public funding.

Nevertheless, to manage the Asylum properly Joseph could not rely on his previously developed skills. One of his first goals was to complete the gaps in his own education by visiting the leading asylums of the day. When he had opened his medical practice in 1846, he had visited Boston and New York, observing the latest techniques in the American hospitals. He did, however, wait the year suggested by Dr. Widmer and then set out in 1855. First he attended the Medical Convention in Boston, followed by visits to asylums in New England, such as the Worcester Criminal Lunatic Asylum in Massachusetts. He had been corresponding since 1853 with Dr. Edward Jarvis, the Medical Superintendent there and a recognized expert in the field. He was surprised at what he found. His first impression of the buildings he saw was that the Toronto Asylum was physically superior to any American asylum.[25]

In 1859 Joseph again braved the Atlantic, except this time he could afford a more luxurious berth and sailing conditions had improved since 1829. First he visited his homeland, renewed old friendships and made new ones which he endeavoured to maintain for the rest of his life. Then he visited the famous Tuke Retreat in Yorkshire, England, and Philippe Pinel's Hospital in France, because he had already read much of the available literature and had many questions. He did not go, unfortunately, to Italy, although he had read much of the Italian research regarding the physiology of the brain. All in all, it was an enriching trip. He accumulated knowledge, ideas, and inspiration, admiring particularly the English asylums of Wakefield and Derby, and the Killarney Asylum in Ireland. He considered many places inferior, such as the Armagh Asylum in the north of Ireland.[26] Throughout his trip, he met several of the leading alienists (the name that was then given to psychiatrists), and returned as the most knowledgable alienist in Canada.[27]

To leave the management of the Asylum for such a long time required great trust. Joseph could do that only because he had persuaded the Visiting Commissioners in 1854 that he needed an Assistant Medical Superintendent. The young graduate he hired was not very competent and resigned, perhaps forced out according to some sources. In 1856 Joseph brought his older brother, Benjamin, from Montreal to be his Assistant. Benjamin had followed Joseph into medicine in 1850, and was anxious to leave Montreal for personal reasons. The position involved a role reversal of earlier years when Benjamin had been Joseph's teacher and employer. By now Ben was getting on in years (sixty-two), and he admired and trusted his younger brother.

By 1860 Joseph's reputation in Canada had been firmly established and he was quoted as an authority not only in Canada but also in the U.S.A. However, before he reached that plateau, he had one major trial to undergo.

A close look at the whole episode provides a vignette of Asylum life in the 1850s and Joseph's approach to problem solving. The pattern of complaining to the authorities and to the local press about the Toronto Superintendent did not stop with Joseph's appointment. In 1856 a former Asylum porter, James Magar, accused the Steward of exposing the female patients to sexual advances. For example, a male patient was inadequately supervised while working on the female ward. A nurse claimed that he was detected with a female in a private room. Magar also reported that a pregnant patient was confined in a straightjacket and was left alone in a place of punishment when she unexpectedly gave birth. When the allegations were brought to Joseph's attention he immediately requested an official investigation by the Visiting Commissioners of the Asylum. The report of the inquiry concluded that there was no valid foundation to the allegations.

It might have all stopped there but for the old animosity between George Brown of the *Globe* and Joseph. Brown was a powerful figure by then. Since founding the *Globe* in 1844, he had become the leader of the Clear Grits, the left wing of the Liberal Reform Party, and had been elected to the government later that year. In 1853, George Brown had criticized Joseph's appointment as being the result of pure patronage. He also had publicized negative comments about Dr. Rolph's Toronto School of Medicine, and had refused to print Joseph's rebuttal. At that time Joseph righteously had declared to the father of one of his patients: "Brown then lied with perfect knowledge of the sin."[29]

In February 1857 Brown chose to publish Magar's allegations, which this time included an attack on Joseph himself, in which Joseph was accused of "villainy, deceit, and tyranny" and "moral pestilence." Interestingly, Brown made no editorial comment at that time. Joseph was upset and decided to interpret this as libel, seeking five thousand pounds in damages. On February 17, Brown published the two letters from Joseph's lawyer, and two lengthy replies. The fight was on![28] Joseph accused Brown of saying he was "guilty 'till he proves his innocence." Brown said Joseph was trying to "coerce the press into silence," and that he must explain the "outrageous doings." A few days later, on February 24, Brown published comments from several other newspapers which criticized Joseph's behaviour. It was a wily manoeuvre. Sides were being drawn up in the press from as far away as Galt. The *Newmarket Era* commented: "The nearer the truth, the greater the libel."

Brown again refused to print Joseph's rebuttal, so Joseph felt he had no choice but to go ahead with the libel suit. The case went to court on April 23 and 24, 1857. Joseph's defence was that Brown personally had not bothered to visit the Asylum where he could have discovered that all was in order, and thus he was harbouring "a vindictive and malicious spirit." Joseph alleged that there seemed to be a conspiracy against himself as well as other Asylum Superintendents, using "the evidence of discarded and degraded menials to crush a man." The recent dismissal of former Asylum superintendents illustrated this point. Most of the jury, however, believed that there was some truth to the accusations. Ten of them voted for Brown and only two for Joseph. So Joseph did not receive any money in damages, nor any apology, and the *Globe* did not publish the Commissioners Report which had exonerated Joseph. Because of the split vote both men had to pay their own legal fees.

The trial revealed some commendable activities on Joseph's part, as well as some questionable ones. Sixty staff in all had been forced out in the past two years, but Joseph replied that they had left because of the enforcement of new stricter rules related to social deportment, safety, theft, and cleanliness (to prevent infectious diseases such as cholera). The stealing of food, for example, had been a major problem in the past. Joseph could not be censured for raising standards. On the other hand it appeared that the four people who made accusations had been fired only after making the allegations of misconduct. It also came to light that Joseph had not spoken to the Bursar for two years, communicating through notes. Because of this lack in communication, Joseph had ended up planning many of the purchases, normally the Bursar's role. Thus he had been too busy to realize that his acting-out female patient was pregnant, although he insisted he had paid her special attention. The birth was therefore a surprise to him. He had kept no formal documentation of coercive measures used by staff, and had required no second opinion before staff used them. He had accepted the resignation of McCullough, an orderly found unsupervised in the female ward, suggesting that he thought the man was culpable. Joseph was unable to deny the allegations completely. Thus the jury did not feel they could exonerate him.

All in all, it appears that the first few years at the Asylum were extremely difficult ones for Joseph. He was learning on the job, as were the staff. Much-needed procedures were lacking. Training was obviously necessary for employees, most of whom had been hired prior to 1853 on the basis of whom they knew rather than on any skill they possessed.

Brown's behaviour was also questionable. He claimed, on February 24, to be responding to the feelings of patients' relatives "tortured by uncertainty which silence must inevitably produce," but in choosing to publish the allegations he was stirring up anxiety deliberately, especially when he added the comment that Joseph seemed to have abused a "sacred trust." Brown was enjoying the "some little excitement in Toronto," despite complaining of "unjust attacks of journals ignorant of the facts." In the *Globe* of April 25, he pressed for a Parliamentary Commission to investigate the situation, suggesting that Joseph should resign as he had admitted that he needed "to gain a verdict" to stay on in his "important and lucrative office." Next Brown published the names of all the jury and how they had voted. Finally he wrote: "It has been proved that Dr. Workman is irascible in temper, that he can use such terms as lying rascal and dirty villain to respectable officers of the Asylum.

Fifty employees tremble at his frown, the irascible, implacable despot." Brown's lawyer accused Joseph of being "thick skinned, tyrannical," controlling and conceited. All this was written in the most popular newspaper of the day!

This was not the end of it. There was a second trial two weeks later, a criminal trial in which the Crown charged Magar, the former porter, with libel. Joseph demonstrated that he had some powerful friends in the case, a fact which Brown commented on publicly. Sir John A. Macdonald, the future first Prime Minister of Canada, was the Attorney General at that time. He must have been consulted before the Crown took on the case. It is well known that he did not care for Brown. This action freed Joseph from the heavy legal expense of a second trial, and he must have felt extremely thankful for that favour. Again Brown came to help Magar. Brown's lawyer argued that some of the same jury should be allowed to serve again, but the Judge refused. Nevertheless, again the jury was split, eleven to one for the defendant.

There is an interesting version of this story provided by the Workman descendants, in which the reputation of Joseph's wife, Elizabeth, was at stake, not that of the Steward. For example, Brown was alleged to hold Elizabeth responsible for the lack of protection from unwanted sexual advances provided the female patients. In the family's version Joseph was reputed to have won the case with the help of Sir John A. Macdonald. This is not entirely incorrect. Although the jury did not support the charge of libel, Joseph survived successfully. The pièce de résistance of the story was the ending in which Joseph ever after kept a strand of Macdonald's hair in a black ribbon on his watch chain. This seems an unlikely act for the usually rational Joseph, who was rarely sentimental about business dealings. Perhaps it was someone else's hair and Joseph jokingly said it belonged to Sir John A. Perhaps it was indeed true, or even that Joseph placed it there to remind himself to be more careful in future. Joseph certainly did form strong and loyal attachments, which is the message that his family remembers.[30]

Joseph weathered this storm, as he had so many others. The citizens of Toronto loved gossip, but they also respected their new Asylum Superintendent; and the political authorities were in no hurry to reopen the controversies of the first half of the decade. There were many who admired Joseph's knowledge and ability to administer such a challenging institution, and they supported him.

Another controversial figure appeared in Joseph's life that year, that of William Lyon Mackenzie. They had had correspondence from 1852 on, ever since Joseph had written to Mackenzie seeking his support on various issues and Mackenzie had responded positively.[31] For example, Joseph's letter of December 1, 1855, reads as follows: "I do not expect that you and I will, in all things, be of one opinion, but I do wish you, most heartily, success in your enterprise. You are too old to learn and I will not presume to tender you any advice. You are a bad boy; but you have done some good in Canada. I have been watching you for twenty-six years, and with all your faults, (shall I say they are 'legion'?), I have always felt a sort of kindred regard for you – for I have seen in your writings and other mental phenomena, a great many things so like my own vagaries, as to make me feel not altogether dissatisfied with myself as being the only human incongruity in this region."

On March 1, 1856, however, Mackenzie wrote Joseph a very angry letter, as a result of an unhappy visit to the Asylum to visit his daughter who had been readmitted a few months before.

Mackenzie had created quite a scene, and Joseph displayed some considerable honesty and self-awareness in his reply: "I was sorry I was absent when you visited the Asylum – and yet not so. Sorry that I had not the opportunity of meeting you, and more especially now that I learn you wished to talk with me – yet not sorry, as I learned you had shewn want of temper, and spoken with unbecoming rudeness, in this habitation of demented woe. I am rash, and you are hot brained; and I think that we might have had a row had we met. I suppose our guardian angels had us both in care."

At the beginning of this confrontation Mackenzie had taken the opportunity to ask Joseph to withdraw his libel suit against Brown. His response to Joseph's lengthy explanation, however, showed that he had understood the situation. It is significant that he did not mention the two court cases in his paper, the *Message*.

These episodes of controversy and scandal reveal certain key characteristics of Joseph's personality. Clearly seen are his fierce tenacity of purpose, his sense of justice, and his ability to defend himself publicly by developing strategies and acting on them. He also appeared to learn from his mistakes. Thereafter he focused more on staff hiring, training and procedures. Criticism from the *Globe* continued off and on during the next twenty-five years, but Joseph was able to withstand it.

CHAPTER EIGHT

Exploring Cause and Effect in Lunacy Reform (1853-1875)

"The time has passed away and can never return, when insanity was regarded and treated as a mere mental derangement, uncomplicated by bodily ailment. How instructive and humbling the thought that functional or structural changes in our organization, often so trivial as to be untraceable, may determine the entire difference between the philosopher and the madman."

J.W.

In 1885 Joseph was described as "the Nestor of Canadian Alienists" by the famous English alienist, Dr. D. Hake Tuke, brother of the Dr. Tuke who visited the Asylum in 1845.[1] This title has been interpreted as meaning the Grand Old Man or the Father of Canadian Psychiatry.

Two detailed studies have been completed in recent years on lunacy reform in Ontario, and both historians include detailed descriptions of Joseph's contribution to the development of psychiatry in Canada. To quote Dr. Rainer Baehre: "Joseph Workman's personal involvement in social and political reform, his sympathy for the forlorn, the downtrodden, and the destitute, his antipathy towards the Upper Canadian establishment, combined with his utopian ideals, both converged and culminated in lunacy reform[2] ... In many respects, he was the Canadian equivalent of Pinel and Tuke."[3] "Sincere, hardworking, indefatigable, urbane, witty, humane, and forthright, his accomplishments were known and recognized both at home and abroad. In an era when reform was very much in the air, Workman breathed it to the fullest ... He effectively laid the groundwork of asylum management in the province (of Ontario), a system which remained relatively intact well into the 20th century. His medical teachings, writings, and public involvement should make him a major figure in Canadian social/intellectual history. But his contribution and exemplary example ... have been all but forgotten." This was despite the fact "Workman did make a significant contribution to Victorian psychiatry."[4]

Dr. Thomas Brown also writes positively about Joseph as "Canada's most prominent nineteenth century alienist," highly admired for his integrity and dedication to kindness.[5] He also commented: "Widmer's assessment of Workman as 'a man of ability, well read, industrious and active' was to prove well-founded, ... Workman ... quickly established himself as THE leading Canadian expert on the subject of the care and treatment of the insane; ... (yet) Workman's approach ... reflected not only his own highly individualistic and pragmatic outlook but also the prevailing psychiatric orthodoxy of the times."[6] He goes on to elaborate how Joseph and the later Canadian pioneers introduced into this continent the leading European ideas rather than developing original theories. (Indeed after Pinel and Tuke no one was truly original until Freud and later Jung radically changed psychiatry.) Dr. Brown adds that "the spirit that Workman had brought to the asylum (was) a spirit of critical inquiry, innovation, and, above all, hope."[7]

During his twenty-two years at the Asylum Joseph spent considerable time testing the European ideas (called "moral treatment") and doing his own research. He explored causes and tried out new treatments for insanity, though, as mentioned above, he did not produce any radically new theory. He became an advocate for humane custodial care of the insane, especially after treatment had failed and patients were diagnosed as incurable, that is, he believed in kindness for its own sake and not just as part of the therapy. Before looking at the treatment component, it is interesting to explore the transformation of Joseph's ideas on temperance, especially as it relates to diagnosis and patient care.

The change in Joseph's attitude to alcohol displays an openness to new ideas, which colleagues reported as being characteristic of him, right into old age. He experimented and then explored the consequences. The Workman family were typical of the Irish Presbyterians and North American reformers who frowned on the evils of alcohol, observing its abuse amongst the struggling Irish poor as well as the wealthier classes. Joseph's brother, Benjamin, prior to his role as Joseph's Medical Assistant, was one of the leaders of the temperance movement in Montreal, a fact which must have created conflict within the Unitarian congregation there because John Molson of Molson's Brewery was also a key member! When Joseph came to Toronto he became involved for many years in the temperance movement and one of his handwritten speeches has been preserved. In it he explores the many diverse problems resulting from intemperance.

His major concern was that alcohol abuse often destroyed not only the family life of the addict but also the physical and emotional health of the imbiber. He observed that the central nervous system was disturbed and the brain cells affected (as evidenced in post-mortems). Even the damage to the fetus was noted. Later on in his career he studied further the connection with insanity and idiocy, commenting that the babies affected were predisposed to mental illness and their intelligence was lowered.[8] He was thus one of the first observers in Canada of "fetal alcohol syndrome."

Joseph also displayed compassion, heightened by the fact that several friends and family members had been afflicted by alcoholism. Believing that encouragement worked better than chastisement "in this noble work of moral and physical regeneration," he was more than just a middle class moralist, desiring to impose social controls.[9] He stressed that it is important to educate people to "their own true nature, and its dignity and divine relations."[10] On the topic of assisting the alcoholic, the clergy of the established churches (especially the Anglican and Roman Catholic) were recipients of his sarcastic tongue, for he described them as being better "hookers of money" than "fishers of men," who needed "to be shown what Christianity is, the way Christ preached it."[11] Having little faith in their leadership, he preferred that lay people would show the way. In addition, he wrote that "some business men were glibly profiting from the miserable addiction of the intemperate," and that alcohol should be the exception to free trade with the U.S.A.

Lack of self-respect was seen by Joseph to be behind much excessive drinking; that is, that intemperance was a result not just the cause of problems. He criticized the prevailing community attitude that regarded the artisans and working classes as inferior, for he believed in the dignity and worth of all human beings. He noticed that several men became innkeepers as a way of becoming upwardly mobile and avoiding the class stigma. This prejudice was repugnant, he wrote, as it destroyed self-respect, the "true basis of temperance."

A major concern at the Asylum was how to sedate the manic and acting-out patients. Joseph had worked hard to remove straight-jackets and other restraints, and to minimise the use of isolation, but he found that something was needed to protect his staff and sometimes the patients themselves. On his trip to England in 1859 he became convinced that his resistance to the use of alcohol had to be reconsidered. So by trial and error he worked out a controlled use of opium and alcohol (usually whisky) as sedatives, replacing the chloral hydrate and bromide of potassium or potash previously used. He also saw alcohol as a tonic for debilitated patients. That same year the Asylum expenses for medicine were a modest $139.33, while that for beer, spirits, and wine were $1,614.72. The press loved the controversy. The *Globe* and the *Mail* of course criticized this indulgence. As before, Joseph rode out the storm, believing that the "comfort, quietude and general health of the institution" was more important than the approval of the press.[12] Benjamin's response to this change in therapy was not recorded. Since he had fought long and hard for the

Montreal temperance movement, there must have been some lively discussions on the topic before Joseph decided to implement his new policy.

While the use of alcohol went up, the use of traditional medication went down. Joseph still experimented with drugs such as opium and quinine for "periodic insanity," but did not find these very satisfactory. More effective was the use of brandy and chloroform to induce eating in patients who were starving themselves. He preferred this method to forcefeeding with a mechanical tube.

Joseph's tenure began with high hopes regarding the new treatment methods. Most of those who supported asylums believed that the new treatment methods would bring about a high 90% cure. The Asylum might then prove to be a good financial investment! That high expectation was a result of reports emanating from English and American treatment centres in the 1830s, often from those with middle-class patients. So Joseph was very surprised and disheartened at his own poor results. He thought he was following the principles of good "moral treatment," in which kindness, good food, fresh air and exercise were combined with a well ordered and pleasant physical environment, and a supportive, structured social community. This was supposed to cure the patients. During the first few years in Canadian asylums, providing good care had accomplished just that. Many (up to 50%) patients had walked away cured.

At first Joseph blamed the lack of space. Soon he became aware that the causes were far more basic and harder to correct. Yet he still demanded more space for humane reasons, arguing "God's charity against man's avarice." He noted that asylums were a drain on the public purse but the purse of a rich country which lacked sympathy, thought and reflection. "It is a heinous offence against the laws of the Divine Ruler of the World … Lunatics require more space than other people."[13]

One way of getting more space was classification and having new smaller centres built away from the Asylum. Thus were removed, (in the jargon of the day) "the idiots" to Orillia, the "criminal lunatics" to Rockwood in Kingston, and the "gentle incurables" to the King's College buildings at the University. Next he would restore to health the "destitute and paupers" and return them to the community, for early on Joseph had advocated a state welfare system, with properly funded almshouses. He was concerned that the Asylum was becoming a dumping ground for all the undesirables and misfits. Hungry men, "dangerous because they required food," were sent under the claim that they were insane.[14] So was a gentle, paralytic woman. He wanted the Asylum to focus on the truly insane who were "acute, improvable or the truly dangerous."[15]

Joseph noticed that frequently the symptoms or effects of both poverty and exposure to cholera were similar to those of insanity, as all were associated with poor physical health. So the first treatment that Joseph offered at the Asylum was individualized medical attention and good nutrition, etc. He described this as focusing on "bodily strength and enriched blood."[16] He was preoccupied initially with the restoration of a healthy digestive and elimination function. He explored the use of various medicines, laxatives and purges, but then decided healthy eating was the answer. He wrote: "I think these revivals in medicine are very like those in religion. Popular appetite demands them, but their permanent good is very trivial."[17] He was more immediately successful with his dental concerns, removing three hundred rotten teeth in his first year.

Joseph was very clear in his annual reports and writings that he had abolished the old treatment methods of cupping and bleeding. Yet, when the descendants of Dr. Ben donated his medical instruments to the Academy of Medicine, they included the old instruments used for cupping and bleeding. There is no record of when they were discarded by Ben, nor why he kept them. Certainly there is no evidence of Ben's having used them at the Asylum.

A detailed classification of patients was to take a long time. Joseph chortled over the causes of insanity he saw listed in earlier documents.

These included: "Grief; Love; Loss of Property; Religious Excitement; Religious Despair ... Religious Controversy ... Reading Religious Books ... Family Quarrels; Jealousy; Fright; Disappointed Affections; Excessive Study; Reading and Fasting; Intemperance; Breach of Promise of Marriage; Suppression of Menses; Slander; Want of Employment; Marriage; Miscarriage; Spirit Rapping; Death of Child ... Husband ... Wife; Business Difficulties; Political; Disputed Boundary; Strong Tea; Eclipse of the Sun; Remorse of Conscience; Inhalation of Nitrous Oxide Gas." He felt these causes were common life experiences and covered most of the population! He added: "Political Excitement would tenant a madhouse in every county, and one of superior class and size in the metropolis. Religious controversy would send in half of the clergy of this province, and large detachments of their congregations."[18]

Joseph concluded that the insane had somatic or physical conditions (caused by genetic inheritance, a blow to the head, illness, bodily disturbances, and so forth), which predisposed them to insanity; the stressful event was often only the trigger to the breakdown. "The time has passed away and can never return, when insanity was regarded and treated as a mere mental derangement, uncomplicated by bodily ailment. How instructive and humbling the thought that functional or structural changes in our organization, often so trivial as to be untraceable, may determine the entire difference between the philosopher and the madman, the chaste matron and the grossly obscene puerperal maniac."[19]

Yet Joseph did not completely throw out these old causes. He saw them now as the triggering event which pushed the patient into insanity. To the physical triggers such as injuries, illnesses and fevers, were added puerperal convulsions, excessive smoking, defective diet and what was called "over-lactation." (The latter does not make sense in today's world, but doctors at that time felt it caused some sort of emotional breakdown.) Joseph studied epilepsy, but he felt there was not necessarily a connection with insanity. If both occurred, however, in the same patient he decided that that person was incurable.[20] Emotional triggers such as overwork and sudden fright were also taken seriously by Joseph as were the "fatal seeds of ruin" to be found in the "corrupt family servant or libidinous book or picture."[21] Last, he added in religious revivals, commenting: "I can hardly believe religion is capable of upsetting any sound mind … many unsound ones are soothed and benefitted by it," but if insanity is latent, participating in religious revivals is dangerous, and the "evil is great and terrible. I need to say it."[22]

Several years later, in 1869, Joseph spoke on the "religious-emotional" type of insanity, and discussed religious revivals and epidemics of "religious commotion." He associated extreme religious fervour with excessive sexual indulgence as well as somatic or bodily abnormality; and connected religious melancholia with masturbation and abnormalities of the sexual organs.[23] Indeed he saw the latter as causes of "religious-emotional" insanity. The speech containing these views was reproduced, and in 1873 reached the editor of the *Christian Guardian*, who was naturally most upset.

It involved a controversial suicide case, and is described in Joseph's Asylum Journal dated March 8, 1873. The case of a Mrs. Muncie elicited a typical scepticism about the role of certain religious teachers. Joseph knew that the patient was insane and suffering from paranoia. He knew punitive religious teaching only aggravated the situation, but did not cause it. Yet he felt compelled to protest. He wrote that only four months prior to her suicide she had been "a good moral Christian woman." But then "she despaired of her own salvation," and Joseph blamed "religious teachers who inculcate the undefined and incomprehensible tenet of sin against the Holy Ghost." He mused that a doctrine that "brought only despair to the good and never disturbed the wicked, might better be avoided than promulgated." He then wrote to the press asking them not to report the suicide since this seemed to encourage imitation. (This is also a current common concern.) He felt the press must lead not follow public opinion, adding that: "Cheap journalism and poor preaching acerbate insanity."[24]

This event resulted in a package of newspaper cuttings being attached to the end of Volume One of Joseph's Personal Diary. At the beginning of March Joseph had made a speech at the inquest of Mrs. Muncie, in which he had stated the above opinions. On March 12 the editor of the *Christian Guardian* wrote a lengthy article which began: "Dr. Workman, the Unitarian Superintendent, seldom fails to improve any opportunity afforded him for throwing out insinuations against religious teachers. He goes out of his way." The paper, however, did publish Joseph's reply despite the fact he was unrepentant. This read: "If the truth offended, the blame could not justly be visited on me. I believe its promulgation must eventually do good." He then described how he gave such a paper in June 1869 at the annual meeting of the American Superintendents and it was well received. They offered no criticism, concluded Joseph, because they had made similar observations. The editor devoted three whole newspaper columns to a response to Joseph's comments. He accused Joseph of being "prejudiced against all earnest types of religious life," and using his position to promulgate his religious ideas. It is significant that Joseph kept all the cuttings in his diary with a comment: "a fine example of religious zeal and truth twisting." He felt Christian fervour was being distorted, and that God's grace and "powers of pardon" were not adequately stressed.

Another such suicide was described in the Journal a year later, on December 1, 1874. One Ellen Newall of Orillia burnt herself as a "propitiation of the salvation of her children" as she felt she had "sinned beyond pardon" and that this would cause the damnation of her children.

In the further search for causes, Joseph spent considerable time and energy completing post-mortem examinations of those who had died in the Asylum. He was seeking not only the cause of death but also looking for some predisposing cause of insanity, some abnormalities in the brain or body. Three hundred and eighty-one dissections were recorded, but he found nothing significant. He read many articles on the findings of the Italian alienists who were seeking physiological causes, and he translated them for North American journals so others might join in the research. It was only a matter of time, he believed, before new technology would reveal the answers, related, he guessed, to lesions, tumours or changes in the brain which were not visible to the naked eye. He inspired others to keep on trying. As he said early in his career at the Asylum, "It is better to plod on patiently than go to sleep under the hypnotic influence of negative prophecy."[25]

One area in which modern therapists would criticize Joseph and his colleagues would be their attitude to masturbation. The nineteenth century view was that this was a major cause of insanity. Joseph wrote and spoke publicly and even warned his children and his grandchildren about this danger. He requested that public health officials and doctors spread the dire warning about "one cause which all over this continent appears to be peopling our asylums with a loathsome, abject and hopeless multitude of inmates. Zeal and intelligence (need to be enlisted) in the exposition and amelioration of this enshrouded pestilence."[26] Thus "moral treatment" could be called moralistic treatment! It is strange that Joseph did not apply his independent judgement and rational thinking to masturbation, and several have criticized him for perpetuating this myth. In this instance he accepted and promoted the prejudice of the day. Only on one occasion did he wonder if its widespread use in the Asylum was a result of mental problems rather than a cause.

Another area in which Joseph did not make much headway was the area of "general paralysis of the insane", known then as "general paresis." There was much discussion in the journals. Some related it to intemperance. An English doctor from Derby named Hitchman connected it with sexual licence. Joseph dismissed the former idea and was unsure about the latter. Were these cause or effect, he wondered.[27] Not until the next century was the full extent of syphilitic infection fully understood and its effect on the central nervous system. In Joseph's era it caused one third of the deaths at the Asylum. Another third was from what we call tuberculosis.

An important contribution Joseph did manage to make in respect to diagnosis was certification. Initially any doctor could certify. Thus the Asylum filled up with social "rejects" from all over Ontario. There was little fiscal responsibility because the province, not the local municipalities, paid. Various alternatives were considered. Finally, in March 1873, legislation was passed which required the signatures of three doctors, independent of each other, and each with two witnesses. In the long run this proved cumbersome but it did solve the problem of "dumping" and made the average doctor more aware of giving a careful diagnosis. The day of detailed definitions and guidelines had not yet arrived. The criterion was a general assessment of the patient's delusions and awareness of reality.

In 1871, the name changed from the Provincial Lunatic Asylum to the Toronto Asylum for the Insane. There were two reasons for this. Other asylums had been built in Ontario and it was no longer the only one in the province. Also of note is the fact that the word lunatic had gone out of style. The alienists who administered the asylums wished to appear modern and scientific, and the use of the word lunatic, suggesting the influence of the moon, sounded superstitious.

CHAPTER NINE

Treatment and Training
(1853-1875)

"On occasion I discover that which unlocks hidden doors and frees the prisoner from his anxiety. One such success makes worth while the hours of toil each day, and wipes clean the slate of failures and disappointments."
J.W.

BELIEVING as he did in the physical predisposition to insanity, Joseph initially focused on the physical body and the physical environment in his treatment program. Part of that environment involved the principles of occupational therapy. Joseph believed that work and exercise in the fresh air were very beneficial, especially for the men, and luckily the Asylum had enough agricultural land for a farm on the property. An additional benefit was that the farm produce cut the food expenses of running the Asylum. The main limiting factor was the cold winter days when the gardens and fields were frozen. Joseph appeared to enjoy the work and planning related to the farm, for his Asylum Journals were filled with maps of the farm layout. His interest probably dated back to his childhood in an Irish farming community, as well as to the skills learned in surveying and in the hardware business. Such things as drains and elevations were marked, for example, in the entry dated October 17, 1872. There was a three acre orchard, pasture land and fields for cultivation. Early in the spring he detailed the crops planned, as well as the soil type and machinery to be used, and in addition the various animals, chickens, pigs, horses and cows kept on the farm. The Asylum even had its very own dairy.

The female patients were not sent to work on the farm but were relegated to the traditional jobs of sewing, cooking and laundry, a role that Joseph did not question, as illustrated by his earlier comments on female education. Their work was deemed necessary to help with all the domestic chores, and keep down the expense of running the institution. The therapeutic value of work was stressed less with the women patients, but it was meaningful for several of them, especially when it meant working for the Superintendent's wife. Elizabeth Workman usually related well to her domestic help.

One patient group which was referred to only in passing was that of the children. Patients as young as eight and ten were mentioned from time to time, but Joseph made no special provision for their treatment, care or education, nor did he raise the issue as one for concern. It is understandable that teenagers might have been living with the regular patients, but it seems incomprehensible to us today that young children would be placed alongside the insane adults.

Spiritual, intellectual and artistic pursuits were not ignored in the treatment program, particularly during those long, dark winters. The building had three chapels, and so Joseph invited the clergy of the three major denominations (the Anglicans, the Roman Catholics and the Presbyterians) to lead services. He saw Sunday worship as necessary for the "consolation and comfort" of most of the patients, but he insisted that attendance be voluntary. The Unitarians were not included, being few in number, but he did invite their dramatic club to entertain the staff and patients. Special outings such as sleighrides or picnics, depending on the season, were arranged for everyone able to appreciate them, as were various celebrations, concerts, and dances in the ballroom. It appeared that male and female patients were allowed to mix on these occasions but the tradition was to keep them separate on the wards. Joseph took advantage of the Annual Ball to invite a group of his medical friends to visit, offering them dinner and a lecture before the dance. This event was frequently written up in the local newspapers.

Joseph himself contributed some works of art for the Asylum, following the advice given by Dorothea Dix in 1854 when she donated coloured engravings for the walls. He read about the beneficial results of art in Italian asylums, and later he himself observed that art had a benign influence on his patients. Regarding reading, he had always believed in education, so he provided a library and forty-one international and national newspapers, most of which were donated by the publishers. Naturally the *Globe* was the exception, and during the 1850s Joseph did not allow it inside the institution. In later years he relented but the Asylum had to pay for the copies. In his official 1874 report Joseph writes: "The Liberal publishers merit the continued gratitude of our people. I wish I could include the *Globe* and the *Mail* in the list but these journals have lunatics enough outside this Asylum to find food for, without adding to the number."

To help patients return to the community, Joseph introduced the occasional use of longterm boarding homes, an innovation at that time. Nowadays the term "halfway house" would be used. He had observed a young fifteen-year-old female patient named Kate improve radically in the Asylum, only to regress immediately she returned to her very moral family. Her bizarre acts included cutting circles in cloth. Joseph did not think her family was responsible for her behaviour, but he noticed that the girl hated her mother. He finally talked to the mother who found a suitable boarding house with employment. Lo and behold, the girl continued to do well. Years later he met her sister, a prostitute, who ended up at the Asylum, and he wondered at the connection. Initially he diagnosed it as "moral mania" or "moral insanity," but eventually he questioned this, observing that all insanity begins with moral alienation, irritability and abberations. Furthermore, he discovered a cousin with similar problems and decided that it was a hereditary strain of insanity.[1]

Thus he advocated taking family histories. This case seemed the closest that he ever came to a Freudian diagnosis of a dysfunctional family. And the whole issue of "moral insanity" was revisited several times by Joseph. He concluded the term should be "insane morality" because the insanity caused the immoral acts. Or to quote Joseph: "Our judgement is often much influenced by our feelings. The latter obscure or warp or completely subjugate the former ... It is a great error to cut the mind up into distinct and independent principalities."[2]

Today moral and immoral acts are analysed differently. Distinctions are made between psychotic (out of touch with reality) and neurotic behaviour (anxiety, depression, stress, and self-defeating responses); and also between feeling much guilt or no guilt. Sociopathic and psychopathic personalities feel little or no guilt about hurting their social group or another person. Joseph was beginning to explore these ideas. He stressed that people who were not insane (meaning psychotic) needed to be held responsible for their actions, an important issue in the legal system.

The use of a boarding or "halfway house" was rare, however. The more common approach, such as was recorded regularly in the early 1870s, was to release patients into the temporary care and custody of relatives and friends. This sometimes developed into an outpatient program, another new concept in asylum management. Other ideas, not new, but which Joseph expanded at the Asylum, were voluntary patients and fee-paying rooms for the wealthier classes.

According to MacDermot in his history, Joseph was modest about his knowledge and never pretended to know more than he actually did. One case in point is Joseph's awareness that some patients recovered without any interventions, and he did not pretend to have cured them. He wrote "Nature possesses self-recuperative power ... (Many people think that doctors use) certain mystical appliances known only to the initiated. They never dream of the curative effect of doing nothing." He observed that the very removal of stress and competition helped some patients regain their self-confidence, so he cut back on medication and encouraged a kind and supportive environment. Therapeutic principles which would later be called group work, were described.[3] But there were many patients who did not respond to any of the approaches. At times Joseph seemed defensive about his overall lack of success in curing patients, but generally he was optimistic that answers would be found eventually. He stressed that diagnoses should not be completed in a hurry. "Time is the great revealer of all secrets," so observation over time by skilled staff was necessary.[4] He stressed that treatment took time, and that too early discharge would result in readmission.

Training of staff was another of Joseph's innovations. After 1853 the Superintendent could hire and fire the staff, with patronage no longer the key criterion for employment. He could then start to build skills, loyalty and team-building, but it would take time, as illustrated by the Magar incident in the previous chapter. He felt kindness sounded easy to learn, but to practise it successfully was a demanding skill, requiring training.[5] Occasionally outsiders were invited to help educate staff. For example, on Dorothea Dix's second visit she gave a lecture to the Asylum nurses. The training of future alienists (psychiatrists) was a priority, so Joseph established three internships at the Asylum, providing free room and board and a small salary. He tried to persuade others to do the same, but in vain. He later read that a similar program was being carried out by the Director of the Asylum of Regio Emilia in Modena, Italy, and used their example to strengthen his case, but still no one else was inspired to copy him. So the government unfortunately discontinued the plan when Joseph retired. There was a response, however, to Joseph's pleas to include some courses in the medical schools in Ontario and in the U.S.A., although no official department of psychiatry was created until many years later. The key experience, however, for aspiring psychiatrists was the internship program, and it launched several important careers, notably those of Charles K. Clarke, Thomas J. W. Burgess, and William Metcalf.

Charles was the son of Joseph's friend, Colonel Clarke of Elora, and came to the Asylum in January, 1874, when he was only sixteen years old. He went on to great fame and fortune, first at the Rockwood Criminal Asylum, then briefly at the Toronto Asylum, and finally at the Toronto General Hospital and at the University of Toronto where he chaired the first Department of Psychiatry. He initiated the Toronto Psychiatric Hospital, the forerunner of the Clarke Institute which was named after him. He later wrote that Joseph was his inspiration and taught him all the basics. (See Chapters Thirteen and Fifteen.) Thomas Joseph Workman Burgess was one of Joseph's godsons from the Unitarian Congregation. (His father was a surveyor who had co-signed the church mortgage with Joseph back in 1854.) Thomas Burgess became the first Superintendent of the Verdun Protestant Hospital in Montreal and wrote a history of Canadian Institutions for the Insane. He too praised his mentor, as "Primus inter Pares."[6] William Metcalf was another brilliant psychiatrist who unfortunately was killed by a patient at the Rockwood Criminal Asylum. His friend and assistant, Charles K. Clarke, was then asked to take over.

Joseph noticed that his colleagues in the U.S.A. were having major problems with "the evils of the spoils system."[7] The asylum jobs there, at all levels, were related to political loyalty and changed with each new change of government. Insecurity and high turnover thwarted good morale and staff development. Unfounded charges were occasionally laid against employees, often for political reasons, and there was no objective investigation completed by trained civil servants. In an effort to help his colleagues, Joseph wrote and spoke about this in his article on management and staff training. He stated that he had escaped much public criticism because of the superior system in Canada, and then fully described the situation at the Toronto Asylum. The appointment of a Board of Inspectors from 1857 to 1867, and a Provincial Secretary and an Inspector after 1867, had provided a trained and non-political level of government to mediate and investigate complaints. In conclusion, Joseph praised the "protecting breakwater, ... government supervision, as my best protection against misrepresentation or revengeful slander."[8] This seemed to contradict the comment in the same article: "Much government, is, in all departments of life, a fundamental evil," and also the comment to his American colleague, Dr. Edward Jarvis, back in December, 1863, when he complained of his "incompetent Board of Inspectors of Asylums and Prisons, pitchforked into office by political influence ... ignorant before and dogmatic after." It would seem that Joseph liked to have a publicly funded system, with appropriately trained personnel administering it, and with some sort of supervision by trained civil servants, but he resented politicians interfering. He did not differentiate clearly the various meanings of government, nor did he seem to remember that his own appointment was the result of patronage.

Similarly, Joseph believed that it was the moral duty of the superintendent to defend all staff from unjust accusations. He added: "Too often power is exercised merely for the sake of demonstrating its possession." He did not comment on his experience of 1857 when the servants accused their boss of being overly authoritarian! (See Chapter Seven, regarding the confrontation with George Brown.) Joseph, however, had learned from his mistakes by instituting tighter hiring and firing procedures. This did not stop him, of course, from disciplining staff when he felt sure that their behaviour was inappropriate. For example, notes in his Asylum Journal dated March 20 and April 11, 1872, describe how he fired two nursing orderlies for retaliating against violent patients who had slapped their faces. Joseph stressed that violence should not be used against violence. Stealing food was initially another concern and he successfully put tough measures in place to counteract it.

His relationship with John W. Langmuir, his Inspector, revealed mixed feelings. Langmuir was very competent and set up an effective and economical system. He fought against giving total control to the medical superintendent and so ran into some conflict with Joseph. At times Joseph praised him, and at other times seemed to resent his control, especially of the purse strings. The resentment was not surprising, considering that two determined men were making decisions concerning issues about which both felt strongly. Yet underneath any conflict seemed to lie a deep respect. When Joseph was accused, towards the end of his career, of still using restraints, it was Langmuir who came to his defence, stating that there was "not a single case of mechanical restraint in the Asylum" and that only three female patients were being kept "secluded."[9] Joseph, however, admitted to the use of restraints when there were not enough staff available to quieten the patient in kinder ways. He denied using seclusion in a "strong room," preferring the use of a crib bed instead.[10] His first choice was that staff take the patient for a walk, outside in the grounds if possible. (The problem was that occasionally the patients escaped or "eloped" from the Asylum.) Not until Richard Maurice Bucke took over the London Asylum was the policy of restraints totally abolished.

Kindness and truth were basic tenets of Joseph's therapy; and even after he realised that they might not cure, he still believed in them as part of good care. He writes in 1858: " Unvarying kindness, never-tiring forbearance, and undeviating truthfulness, are the cardinal moral agencies now employed in every well-conducted Lunatic Asylum; and surely no remedies could be found less expensive, or more easy of appliance. The superintendent who does not find these the most potent curatives has certainly chosen a wrong position. Recourse to harshness in any form or degree must indicate not merely an ill-natured act but also the utter absence of common sense and correct information. To live among the insane is but to be irresistibly constrained to pity and love them; and, when once this bond is established between physician and his confiding family, the task of government becomes, so far as THEY are concerned, a labour of inconceivable pleasure."[11]

Joseph practised what he preached for observers on the wards stressed Joseph's perpetual kindness and gentleness to his patients. The comments also suggested that he was so loved and revered by his patients that they would hesitate to disobey him. He certainly spent many extra hours just talking and listening to them. Dr. Thomas Burgess wrote in his history: "It was my good fortune to have spent nearly two years in the Toronto Asylum as clinical assistant under Dr. Workman. During that time I can scarcely recall an evening on which this gifted man did not pass an hour or more in one or other of his wards, the centre of a circle of patients, for whom he never failed to find some topic of interest by which to divert them from their morbid thoughts."[12]

In a letter to William Lyon Mackenzie Joseph expressed the same sentiment but in a very self-righteous vein: "I solemnly declare that my duties amongst my patients are to me a source of happiness beyond all sublunary enjoyments. I love my patients – and they love me – they are honest, truthful, grateful. I detest the world outside these walls. You had rather be an editor – I had rather restore reason. You rejoice in the function of distracting it – God help the world!"[13]

However, while Joseph advocated kindness and the minimum use of restraints, he was also very aware of the latent violence in some of his patients, and the danger this presented to other patients and to the staff. In the above mentioned letter to Mackenzie he described an incident in which a patient had planned to attack him (Joseph) with a knife. He felt a disgruntled employee had incited the man.

In the history of the first superintendents of the Toronto Asylum, one problem repeatedly listed was their inability to relate to the patients of the poorer classes. The Asylum had a preponderance of such and they were increasingly poor Irish immigrants. Benjamin Workman was described in the annals of the Montreal Unitarian congregation as having the rare ability to relate to rich and poor alike, and also to Catholic as well as Protestant, and Joseph seemed to have that same skill. This ability gave Joseph and Benjamin an edge over their predecessors and probably contributed to the affection in which most of their patients held them.

Joseph played an important role not only amongst Canadian psychiatrists but also with the Americans. His senior status in the Association of American Asylum Superintendents was one example. His often humorous speeches and numerous articles were influential. The annual meeting of the Association was held in Toronto in 1871, and afterwards the members wrote a resolution "That our eminent and respected colleague, Dr. Joseph Workman, has won the honourable position he holds in our speciality by a wise comprehension of the multi-form duties of his arduous office, and by a courageous energy which has continued unappalled in the face of no slight obstacles, we now readily understand, after personal inspection of the great institution over which he so worthily presides. We recognize in its vast dimensions, in the spaciousness and comfort of its new apartments, in the tasteful adornment of its grounds, and the systematic provision for out-door occupation and amusement of his patients, the serious nature of the problems committed to him, and the masterly skill with which he has solved it."[14]

On another occasion, however, Joseph was upset when his American colleagues scoffed at his recommendation that short-term patients be separated from chronic cases. He decided that they were afraid that this would diminish the role and importance of the asylum in the life of the community.

In 1890 the American Journal named the *Alienist and Neurologist* published an article on Joseph written by David Boyle, the Curator of the Royal Ontario Museum. In it he commented: "Dr. Joseph Workman, whose photograph graces the initial pages of this journal, was one of its earliest collaborators, and he has continued a constant, faithful and entertaining workman on the collaboratorial staff of the *Alienist and Neurologist* to this day ... His long clinical experience, large medical discernment and ripe scholarship have made him a power and a charm in the wide and widening circle of our readers. He is known ... by the always appropriate and entertaining translations ... The most critical of our many readers having always approved the judiciousness of his selections, applauded the beauty of his diction and approved his criticisms."[15] Boyle had other reasons, however, to like Joseph. He had rented one of Joseph's houses on Mutual Street and Joseph had helped pay the medical fees for his daughter, Dr. Susanna Boyle.

The articles Joseph translated are extremely numerous, mostly from Italian journals (where the focus was on the anatomy and physiology of the brain). Initially he could not get his translations published, but once he retired, the *Alienist and Neurologist* and the *Canadian Lancet* printed most of them. The only translations published earlier were two German articles (one in 1864 and another in 1865). On a later occasion, in 1884, a Spanish translation was printed, as well as a Danish poem. Joseph was certainly demonstrating his prowess in languages. He also wrote many articles full of his own professional opinions. All in all, this shows that he contributed theoretically to the development of his profession as well as offering practical models and leadership. In addition, he enjoyed public speaking and teaching, and took pleasure in inspiring young physicians entering the profession.

All these qualities contribute to the portrait of him as one of the most esteemed and best loved of all the nineteenth century Canadian doctors.[6]

Illustrations

1. Home of the Workman family, Ballymacash, Ireland.

2. Typical cottage of the early 19th century.

3. Joseph's school at Mullacarten.

4. Dunmurry Non-subscribing Presbyterian Church

5. Workman pew in far corner of Dunmurry Church.

6. Portrait of the Rev. Henry Montgomery.

7. 1847 sketch of King Street East, Toronto.

8. Sketch of the Asylum at 999 Queen Street West, Toronto.

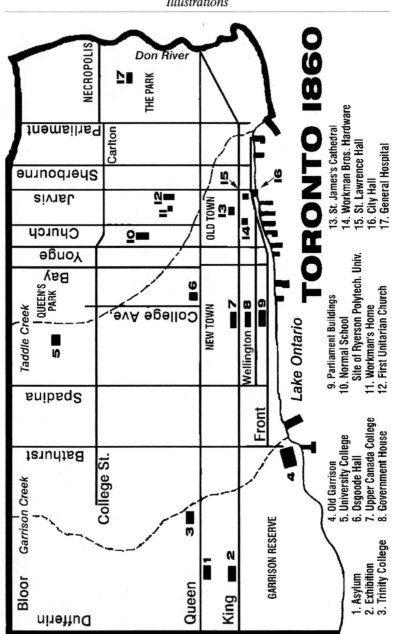

TORONTO 1860

1. Asylum
2. Exhibition
3. Trinity College
4. Old Garrison
5. University College
6. Osgoode Hall
7. Upper Canada College
8. Government House
9. Parliament Buildings
10. Normal School
    Site of Ryerson Polytech. Univ.
11. Workman's Home
12. First Unitarian Church
13. St. James's Cathedral
14. Workman Bros. Hardware
15. St. Lawrence Hall
16. City Hall
17. General Hospital

10. Joseph as a young man.

11. Joseph in his working years.

12. Joseph's official portrait.

13. The senior years.

14. The senior years.

15. The senior years.

16. Catharine Workman.

17. Elizabeth Workman.

18. Dr. Ben Workman.

19. Dr. Charles K. Clarke.

20. Four of the Workman Children (L to R: Florence, William, Anna, Fred).

21. The children of William and Jane Workman.

The Power of Words

"One can ask why the Deity, when he made man, chose not to make him whole. One can understand why He chose against perfection, for what glory is there in praise from the perfect, who are incapable of choosing not to praise. Yet to make man with so fragile a thing as the human mind is, to me, incomprehensible."
J.W.

JOSEPH loved the power of words. He loved the spoken word, and he loved to read and to write. With whatever free time he had, he enjoyed exploring the meaning and use of words. He loved to record brief musings on the meaning of life and his life's work, such as is given above. His writings were in the form of letters, articles, translations, and especially entries in his diaries, of which, at one time, he kept three. One was that of the Asylum, one was a personal diary, and the third was a weather journal.[1] He said that he often wrote for four hours a day, sometimes well into the night, going with relatively little sleep. The diaries reveal a fascination with recording detail as well as the ability to see the whole picture. They also reveal a cautious streak, a hesitancy to reveal his true feelings about people close to him, as if he were aware that posterity and his family members might read his comments. This was not surprising because his father and brother Benjamin had kept diaries, and Joseph had had access to them.

Growing up in Ireland with its tradition of oratory and poetry was probably an important factor influencing not only Joseph's love of words but also the flavour of his humour. His language tended to be colourful, even exaggerated, with an ironic or sardonic edge, in many ways typically Irish. Usually there was no hostility directed at a particular person or group, but when riled he certainly used a bitter sarcasm to demolish his critics. As mentioned earlier, this character-istic was condemned by some of the newspaper critics during his early days in Toronto. Joseph also used hyperbole for dramatic effect, to entertain and make his point at the same time. Yet he knew when to be serious and even lyrical, as demonstrated by the quotation above.

For Joseph the written word fulfilled several needs. First, he used letter-writing to maintain many of the relationships important to him. It is uncertain if he wrote to friends in Ireland after he first emi-grated, but certainly, following his visit in 1859, he kept regular con-tact through letters. A few Irish friends even managed to visit Canada. After he left Montreal, he wrote regularly to the family members left behind as well as to several of his medical colleagues from McGill. Though his first years in Toronto were busy ones, he had time to in-dulge his love of reading for he had few friends in town with whom to socialize and few distractions in those days before the advent of the telephone, radio, and television. Gradually, however, he turned more and more to creating his own flow of words. He developed a skill in writing editorials, letters to the editor, and speeches on such topics as temperance and political issues. Later, he turned again to the art of letter-writing when seeking guidance from experienced senior medi-cal colleagues. For example, saved for posterity has been his corre-spondence with Dr. Edward Jarvis of the Worcester Asylum in Mas-sachusetts. As Joseph developed his own medical expertise this rela-tionship became more of a friendship, but he continued to use Dr. Jarvis as a sounding board for his ideas and opinions, especially when seeking an American perspective.

Also preserved were several letters exchanged with colleagues in Toronto, Dr. John Rolph and Dr. Christopher Widmer. To Dr. Rolph he confided details of personal financial problems, such as his need to borrow money from Thomas, his brother in Montreal, when the government was slow to pay him his expenses on the Royal Commission. Dr. Rolph also offered to help Joseph on occasion. Hence Joseph's willingness on October 30, 1871, to lend Dr. Rolph the sum of $400. He commented in his personal diary that even if the money were not returned, it was well spent in the cause of friendship.

Another doctor to whom he wrote was Dr. Howitt of Guelph. In this case Howitt was another "free thinker" like Joseph whose views were often criticized by others, but Joseph insisted that his "piety was deep, fervent and humble."[2]

Joseph knew two of the well-known younger doctors of the period. His diary entry of August 8, 1884, states that he spent three days with the young and later famous psychiatrist, Dr. Richard Maurice Bucke, on a site inspection proposal in Montreal. On other occasions they worked together on forensic consultations, Bucke being the Superintendent of the new London Asylum. In 1876 Joseph drily commented: "Dr. Bucke was doomed to share with me the infliction of a full measure of that organ's classic slang." The organ referred to was Joseph's chronic critic, the *Globe*, who censured them both for declaring a murderer insane, and thus escaping the death penalty. The closeness of the relationship was not mentioned, but a certain warmth was suggested in a letter sent by Bucke to Joseph on the occasion of Joseph's eighty-seventh birthday. Bucke was also a fellow pall-bearer at the funeral of the young Dr. William Metcalf, who was murdered in 1885 by a patient at the Rockwood Criminal Asylum in Kingston. Another pall-bearer was the internationally famous doctor, Sir William Osler. He was involved with the Canadian Medical Association as was Joseph in the late 1870s, but Joseph did not comment on that relationship either. On September 25, 1884, however, Joseph attended the farewell dinner for Osler before that eminent man left for the University of Pennsylvania, and later he wrote in his diary: He "received more laudation than his modesty could well sustain."

One of Joseph's closest friends was Lieutenant-Colonel Charles

Clarke of Elora, Dr. C. K. Clarke's father. He was a newspaperman who entered politics and became well-known in Ontario as a Provincial Member of Parliament for twenty-eight years and Clerk of the Legislature for eight years. Their exchange of letters has been preserved, as have the many entries in Joseph's diary mentioning this relationship. For example, on March 23, 1867, he recorded a two day visit from Clarke, and noted that Clarke brought nine books on Lincolnshire with him. They spent many hours discussing the origin of words. After he left, Joseph read Luke's Gospel in Anglo-Saxon, followed by the *Saxon Chronicles*, books on the derivation of Gaelic and Scottish words, and two European histories. Whenever these two men exchanged boxes of books, the contents were carefully listed. On one occasion they included the Koran, Bede's Ecclesiastical History and such authors as Ben Jonson, Pepys, Burns, Shakespeare and Pope. Evolution, Darwin and Huxley fascinated them, an interest also shared by Joseph's brother, Thomas. Birds and nature, as well as politics were always favourite topics. Later on, Joseph recorded reading philosophical books as *Modern Science and Modern Thought*, *The Idea of God* and *Destiny of Man* by John Fiske. A description of the hospital work of Florence Nightingale was also mentioned, the new role for female nurses being of particular interest to him. Absent was any book on music or art, and novels were nowhere to be found. Joseph probably considered the latter to be frivolous, but he did enjoy poetry and memorized his favourite passages.

Occasionally Joseph's diary contained comments on the life of the city around him, a reminder that the character of Toronto was rapidly changing. A social event of interest to later generations was the near presence of what was soon to become, in 1878, the Exhibition Grounds. On September 26, 1874, when Joseph saw retirement looming, he complained that the showgrounds disturbed his peace and quiet, and hoped any exhibition "will never be held here again in my lifetime." He described the growing urbanization around him, noting, in December, 1871, "the young fry crowding into the large towns in quest of easier and lazier modes of life. Early marriages are expensive transactions since silks have displaced cottons, and pianos, spinning wheels and milk buckets."

Joseph was interested in national and international affairs, especially those south of the border. In 1869 he wondered why the American government "promotes immigration instead of procreating their own inheritors." He observed that "provoked abortions" were common in the U.S.A., but not yet in Canada. (He considered the doctors involved to be "black sheep.") Sometimes he was very critical of what he saw. For example, on December 14, 1891, following an extensive trip through the States, he reacted to the city of Chicago by describing it as a "huge den of scoundrels, sharks, pickpockets and other human cattle ... (but) perhaps I am prejudiced." Despite such comments, he was not a strong Canadian nationalist. This was clear in a letter he wrote to his American friend, Dr. Edward Jarvis: "I am no politician – my aspirations are altogether cosmopolitan – I hardly care under what flag my grandchildren live, provided it be the standard of liberty and of BROAD human brotherhood ... (I) only pray that whatever change may come it may come in PEACE ... I was taught from my cradle to venerate the names of Franklin, Washington, and though I love Victoria with an unquenchable loyalty, and would myself die in her service, I am not blind to geographic landmarks and to the march of western events – Our institutions, our habits of thought, our go aheadiveness – all not so very unlike yours, as many New England men imagine – (though) we, indeed move more slowly."[3] Certainly the American superintendents accepted him as one of their own, and were known to describe him as their "Nestor of students of mental disease."[4]

(As an aside, it is of interest that Joseph gave a speech in the States in which he praised George III, pointing out that his insanity stimulated much public interest in mental illness and helped create the U.S.A. The British picked up the item and discussed it at length, while it was strangely ignored this side of the Atlantic.)[5]

As might be expected from the above sentiments, Joseph was sceptical about Canadian Confederation, writing on July 1, 1867: "Today is celebrated the Confederation of the British American colonies. May our new state of political existence realize all the benefits promised by the promoters of the measure! My fears, however, overweigh my hopes." Later in 1883, he suggested that Sir John A. Macdonald "dragged us all, kicking and screaming, into this Confederation, about which I had my grave doubts."[6] Unfortunately he did not elaborate.

Sometimes Joseph appeared rather arrogant in his written comments, assuming that he was right and his opponents wrong. At other times he displayed the humility that his friends insisted was characteristic. Sometimes he just seemed to be enjoying the power and flexibility of words for their own sake. His attempts at humour were not always appreciated. For example, George Brown of the *Globe* was very critical of Joseph's attempts to liven up his annual Asylum reports with humour. A sample of this is found in the Appendix. Joseph resented censure from anyone and particularly from George Brown, but on July 1, 1871, he pondered on the inevitability of being criticized, writing in his diary: "The less I say as to my success the more satisfaction in all probability to my successors. Indeed it would be a great pity that they should be placed in the awkward position of having nothing to find fault with. A large portion of my work must be altogether invisible."

Joseph, however, was not slow in criticizing others, especially when he felt they exhibited hypocrisy. When provoked he often resorted to sarcasm. His comment on Sunday visitors to the grounds (found in the Appendix) illustrates this point. In this situation his concern was their lack of empathy for the mentally ill, for he himself was seldom other than kind to the patients. Other examples of his sarcasm can be found in his diary where he recorded witty comments he was proud of making. On 9 September, 1879, he wrote a description of colleagues at a meeting, that "had they held their tongues, they might have passed for wiser men." In a speech made in 1883 he commented: "There were men then, there are in every age, who every time they spoke, the sum total of human knowledge was greatly diminished."[7]

George Brown naturally did not escape Joseph's pen. He had become a politician and one of the "Fathers of Confederation" in 1867. In March 1880 someone shot him in the leg and he died in May from the infected gunshot wound. Joseph wrote of him in his diary: "Much lamented, yet I doubt if the weeping of some is quite unaffected. *Sic transit qui multos occidit. Requiescat in pace, si placeat pax illi.*" (The Latin translates as: "So passes the one who kills many. May he rest in peace, if peace should be pleasing to him.") Joseph then adds: "Dr. D. Clarke said the weight of his brain is 56 ounces." But six years later (diary item dated April 26, 1886), Joseph realized that forgiveness was the real issue. He did not mention George Brown by name, but he was probably thinking of him when he wrote these words: "I have great reason to be thankful to a Gracious Providence for many precious blessings, among which has been that of a tender, loving wife and good children. We have had our share of troubles. It is impossible for any man or woman to pass honestly and fearlessly through life, and especially public life, without making enemies. I have had a few, but they have nearly all passed over to the great majority, and now I would rather remember whatever was good in them than remember their faults. None but the faultless should be unforgiving and surely I am very far from ranking in this class."

His comments two years later about John Howard were unusually magnanimous. Possibly he was now practising the forgiveness that he had recently preached. He wrote on June 30, 1888: "With Dr. Covernton I visited J. G. Howard of Colborne Lodge, High Park. He is now eighty-four. He has been a man of exemplary integrity and unvarying veracity. It has, however, been my opinion that his bestowal of so much valuable land on the City of Toronto was a rather Quixotic adventure ... Twenty years after his death his munificence will be little thought of … just so will it be worth John G. Howard's memory, but he has been true to the promptings of his own nature." History has proved Joseph wrong. Howard is remembered for his gift. The city did give him a pension in exchange, but it was a small price for the land. Howard donated 165 acres, which became the core of High Park, now 400 acres in size.

As Joseph grew older he sadly listed the dates of passing of all his friends and colleagues. For him the pattern of record keeping had been well established, and he kept writing up until 1892 when his hand began to waiver. His daughter, Florie, added a few items in his diary during the following year. By that time his energy was directed into enjoying the letters and newspaper clippings others sent to him. He also took pleasure in reading his favourite books right up to the very end of his life. Indeed he had spent his last day on a translation, and only an hour before he died, he assisted a friend in looking up a quotation from Robert Burns, the Scottish poet.

CHAPTER ELEVEN

The Weather Buff

*"Drop in barometric pressure. Storm to the west. Last night the
female patients of No. 7 were very noisy and restless.
The night nurses' book reports no less than eleven
cases of high excitement."*
J.W.

JOSEPH began his Weather Journals before any of the other diaries,
suggesting that the topic was of keen interest to him.[1] He started
them in 1860 and maintained them for thirty-four years, filling four
leather bound volumes. (There is the possibility of course that
Joseph had other personal and professional journals going at that
time which were destroyed or have gone missing.) Weather diarists
were common in the nineteenth century but few had such a keen
knowledge as Joseph. A knowledgeable commentator recently
wrote that "perhaps the most significant contribution to the collection of data for the last century are his comprehensive summa-
ries of the daily weather."[2]

The first regular scientific observations in Canada began in
Montreal in the 1740s. Scientific measurements involved the use
of the thermometer and barometer recently invented in Italy. When
the British Government decided to establish an observatory and
weather services in Canada, they found that Montreal was not suitable because of geomagnetic conditions in the St. Lawrence valley.
For this reason Toronto was chosen, and in 1839 Lieutenant C. J.
B. Riddell of the Royal Artillery set up an observatory, first in Fort
York and later on the grounds of King's College. Weather observations and comprehensive tests for terrestrial magnetism were com-

pleted every two hours. This developed into a national service, though for a decade it was at a very beginning level. In 1855 the Director of the Observatory tried to arouse interest in the collection of data from all over eastern Canada but initially he met with little success. The new electric telegraph could have been used to transmit data from one location to another and thus predict the onset of storms, but it was not until 1876 that the first storm warning was issued and 1877, the first general forecast. Storm warnings were announced by the display of wicker baskets of different shapes and sizes on poles at or near harbours, a system operative for the next half century.[3]

Joseph would have visited the Observatory in 1850 when he was investigating the finances of King's College and calling on all the agencies renting land. They probably discussed the latest in instruments, and how to interpret the results. An interesting comment was found attached to Joseph's Journals, written by Dr. Stupart, Head of the Canadian Meteorological Services, when studying them in 1922. He pointed out that Joseph's readings all corresponded to the official records except that Joseph's barometer was set a little low.

Egerton Ryerson also became an enthusiastic weather buff. As Superintendent of Education for what is now Ontario, he directed all the grammar schools to make weather observations for the year 1858, and as a result twelve new stations were established. This was after Joseph's official school tenure was over but he still followed educational events with interest.

There were no statements as to why Joseph liked to record the weather. Perhaps the four mile walks to and from school in his childhood awakened his interest, or perhaps it was the years of surveying in Ireland when he was out of doors for hours on end. His intense involvement in the Asylum farm augmented this interest. His work in psychiatry, however, added a different dimension. Joseph often recorded the influence of weather changes on the patients.

For example, on November 19, 1860, he wrote that there was a drop in barometric pressure, a storm coming in from the west, and "last night the female patients of No. 7 were very noisy and restless ... eleven cases of high excitement." Then on April 6, 1861, he observed that "the atmospheric influence is disagreeable and has an evidently irritating tendency over many of the patients."

The weather journals contained entries every few days. To the barometric pressure, temperature and wind readings were added descriptions of clouds, birds, trees, and stars. The planting and sowing of the farm crops were noted as was the date of the first blossoms and the first robins and swallows. On June 14, 1875, he observed that the potatoes were blackened by the frost in a sheltered part of the field. He added: "This fact is of scientific value. It was known to me over thirty years ago. It appears that in motionless air, the cooling down process goes on accumulatively." Without doubt this reminded him of the potato famine in his homeland and of the many Irish who perished as a result.

Frequently added to the journals were newspaper clippings on the weather as well as detailed descriptions of historic events from all over North America which were affected by unusual weather patterns. Joseph was fascinated with the topic. For example, on September 7, 1860, he recorded that the Prince of Wales was expected to arrive at Kingston by water but a storm was anticipated. Elsewhere, carefully preserved, was an article written by Thomas Workman, Joseph's brother in Montreal, who had been a Loyalist volunteer during the 1837 Papineau Rebellion in Quebec. Thomas wrote a detailed account of the bitterly cold weather and its influence on the outcome of the Rebellion. For example, several of the soldiers in Colonel Gore's army had to walk on frozen mud without boots or shoes, arriving so exhausted and stressed at the village of St. Denis that they were defeated by the rebels; however, the next month, the Ottawa river was sufficiently frozen to allow the well equipped government forces to cross on an ice bridge and this time defeat the rebels at St. Eustache.

On November 12, 1880, Joseph included in the journal his letters to the press about a much publicised accident on Lake Ontario in which many people drowned. Joseph suggested the Captain of the boat in question (the *Zealand*) showed "self-satisfied contempt" for meteorological science, by ignoring the weather signs which should have alerted him. Joseph demonstrated his skilled powers of observation and a profound understanding of wind currents, writing: "At this hour a strong northerly wind, with rapidly flying scud, was blowing; but up above the scud-run there was a majestically flowing dense cloud field, moving from S.S.W. to N.N.E. Anyone who has attentively watched these opposite cloud-runs, and has noted their relation to barometric descents, must have felt convinced that a severe storm was coming up from the region whence the upper current was flowing." Modern meteorologists would support Joseph's conclusions.[4]

Clouds and wind currents were of particular interest to Joseph. On January 13, 1877, he wrote to the *Mail* and signed himself "Fiat Justitia." This was part of a debate with a well-known Mr. Vennor of *Vennor's Almanac*, Montreal, whose predictions were usually so incorrect that Joseph considered him a "reckless generaliser." As mentioned, Joseph had long observed that the upper wind currents in a storm ran contrary to the surface winds. He pointed out to Mr. Vennor that the wind, "a mere surface current," might come from the east but the snow storm or rain carrier came from the west. Mr. Vennor wrote a personal reply, saying that might be true in Toronto but was not the case in Montreal!

Joseph's scorn was heaped not only on Mr. Vennor. On July 6, that same year, he wrote: "In Manitoba the season has been so very wet as to prompt the clergy to pray for its cessation. It is always prudent to defer the praying until the rain belt is about to move off, just as in Lower Canada the priests used to wait till the caterpillars had devoured all the tree foliage before making their procession for the purpose of driving off the pest."

On November 12, 1880, Joseph wrote a letter to the *Mail*, signing himself "An Observer." He suggested "A very little plain instruction of even our common seamen ... would enable them to foresee and to escape from many of those perils which they now encounter in an utterly unprepared nautical and mental state."

This love of meteorology was shared with family and friends whenever they seemed interested. For example, Dr. Andrew Fisher of the Malden Lunatic Asylum at Amherstburg, began in December, 1860, to collect temperature, wind and barometric readings three times a day, and compare them with those at the Toronto Asylum. He continued this intensive work for only a year, but they received great publicity by being printed in the *Leader* newspaper in September of that year. Two other young doctors also became interested, Dr. C. K. Clarke (who later sent Joseph weather jottings from Kingston), and Joseph's godson, Dr. Thomas J. W. Burgess, who became well known as a naturalist in the Muskoka region of Ontario. Joseph involved other friends too. On May 6, 1880, he obtained a new aneroid to measure elevations. This he took to Elora on one of his visits to Colonel Clarke, and together they tried it out in the area around the Clarke home. His own family enjoyed the application rather than the theory behind the weather, for his wife Elizabeth was an avid gardener, specialising in flowers, and their oldest son, William, had taken up botany as a hobby.

Joseph kept up this activity for thirty-four years. When he became frail he would sit by the window and record his observations. When his hand began to waver in 1892, one of his daughters, Florence (Florie), wrote the entries instead. Items became more personal, such as her description of the soot from the soft coal used in their furnace. At that time they lived on Mutual Street, in an elegant terrace house (its style similar to the still standing Mackenzie House, only their home had a large shed at the back). She often sat with Joseph at the rear window overlooking the back gardens and the Unitarian church grounds, and particularly memorable are her descriptions of the beautiful cherry, apple and locust (acacia) blossoms every Spring. For the ten years following his death she continued to enter comments or attach newspaper cuttings but her entries did not match the quality of her father's observations. Her sister's daughter, Kitty Kennedy Lavelle, inherited the four leather-bound journals and helped preserve them for posterity.

CHAPTER TWELVE

Joseph the Sleuth

*"So, rather than being a simple task, I find my role more taxing than
I was led to believe. I prefer such digging into the tangled skein
of life to be left to our English novelists, of whom there are
many of stature. And yet, just such delving into what was
to understand what is, is perhaps the basis of that
craft which I follow at the Asylum."*
J.W.

FORCED to resign? The *Sun* newspaper of December 6, 1875, stated
that the opposition parties in the Ontario Legislature questioned
the odd circumstances of the resignation of the highly esteemed
Dr. Workman, and added that, ever since the summer, the newspapers had been debating the issue. Joseph had handed in his resignation on January 7, and left in July. His successor, a Scot named
Dr. Gowan, had attempted suicide with a drug overdose (ten grams
of morphine) only weeks after starting his tenure, resulting in the
opposition's request for all the official letters and documents related to the situation.

Joseph himself was tight-mouthed and enigmatic, even in his
diaries. In his personal diary he wrote that he was resigning "for
reasons best understood by myself," but would remain a consultant "provided the position involves no participation in the management and no connection with the inspector." Yet he had described Langmuir, the inspector, as a "good friend" and a "protecting breakwater," so it is unlikely petty officialdom was the main
cause.

On July 19, 1875, Joseph wrote in his personal diary: "Many troubles have befallen me but above all the slanders of a brutal newspaper press." As already mentioned, both the *Globe* and the *Mail* had enjoyed criticizing him publicly for a variety of things: for indirectly encouraging promiscuity; for the abuse of alcohol; for being a Unitarian (November 21, 1869); and for the florid style of his annual reports (for that of December, 1874, see the Appendix). But Joseph had experienced the censure of the press ever since he had written for the *Mirror* and had argued for such issues as free and secular schooling. He had fought with wit and humour in the past, so it is puzzling why he should feel unusually hurt now.

One major point ignored by colleagues was Joseph's age. He was forty-eight when he started at the Asylum and seventy at his retirement. One observer, however, had commented that Joseph looked only fifty-five at that time, suggesting that most people were unaware of his true age. Another factor in the puzzle was the age of his kindly older brother Ben, who was still the Assistant Medical Superintendent. The Workman family have a letter written from Joseph to his daughter-in-law, Jane Clarke Workman, stating: "I retired because it was the only way to get Ben to retire." In a similar vein he had written a year before to his colleague, Dr. Edward Jarvis: "My brother is poorly now, almost worn out, indeed wholly so, would he but believe it." This was not surprising since Ben was now eighty-one.

Joseph also shared with Jarvis concerns about his own "wear and tear ... Retirement is a personal necessity."[2] On one occasion his student and friend, Dr. C. K. Clarke, seemed to have no doubt about the matter and commented that Joseph retired "on the grounds of advanced age and resulting consciousness of inability to discharge the largely increased duties of his office." Yet at another time Clarke wrote: "He retired, angered at the political game being carried on by Mr. Langmuir (the Inspector) who tried to act the lay dictator."[3] Joseph, meanwhile, seemed to enjoy all the speculation and the idea that people thought him much younger than he was. He even denied feeling tired. This touch of pride or vanity was evident in his speech to the young Toronto medical students in 1883, in which he stated: "I retired, not because I was old. Seventy is not old. But because of those who knew the least, saying the most and having the power to be listened to by those who should know better."[4]

Certainly Joseph did not appear tired for he promptly jumped into a busy schedule of forensic court work, lecturing and writing. His contributions to the world of medicine thus continued, but took a different direction. In addition to the above, he was elected as an examiner for the Medical Council from 1876 to 1880, testing medical students in midwifery, pediatrics and what we now call gynaecology. This was clearly a labour of love, and not for the money. He had been given a good pension or retirement allowance, although in true style he had to battle to receive what he considered his full due. (He had been given $3500 and Ben $1500, but he managed to have $500 added to each sum.)

Joseph commented in his Asylum Journal on December 16, 1873 that he had started consulting in forensic work while still working at the Asylum. When the government offered to pay only the expenses for Joseph's additional work, he noted, wryly: "If my services are worth no more than this livery, I present them gratis to the Department of Public Justice." This involvement with the criminal court was a natural extension of his expertise in psychiatric assessments. He was a natural sleuth. His approach to solving crimes was similar to that of Sherlock Holmes: deductive reasoning, observation of details, and analysis of motive. His own emotions were usually under tight control, and, coupled with his strong sense of purpose and a lively sense of humour, this helped him cope with the more grisly aspects of the suicides and murders. He was an excellent witness in the court room, and, according to Dr. C. K. Clarke, a "facile princeps" (meaning "easily the best"). The only thing he resented was the time spent away from his books and translations, particularly the hours spent in travelling.

Joseph was against capital punishment, calling it a futile deterrent, although he granted that the final decision needed to be left to the "will of society."[5] He was very critical of allowing the young to witness executions, a "source of moral contamination. No principle can operate so effectively to the prevention of murder, as the inculcation of the sacred character of human life."[6] He also criticized the Canadian system in which the accused was sentenced before his sanity was assessed by a medical doctor. In contrast were the French and American systems where the diagnosis came first. In many of the cases in which Joseph was involved, the crime was murder and the penalty death by hanging. In such circumstances he was suspicious of accused persons who claimed to be mad. In contrast he had observed that nearly all insane patients insisted they were normal. He called the former group "imposters."

Joseph seemed to enjoy the challenge of forensic work and travelled all over Southern Ontario. He did complain, however, that, when his opinion differed from the popular one, "the entire indignation and ponderosity of the Bar, the Bench, the Press, the Pulpit and the blood-demanding Populace will come down on you as a moral avalanche, and you will be stigmatized as an apologist of crime ... Medical experience comes into collision with legal tradition and popular prejudice ... Insanity displays itself, not in thought, but in acts."[7] Joseph noticed that the most publicized crimes were the most heinous, and he believed that these were usually the result of dementia or brain damage. For example, Erastus Hotchkiss was sentenced to hang but Joseph decided he had brain damage (resulting from a kick on the head from a horse) and was therefore insane. The local newspaper protested vigorously.[8] Joseph had never run away from controversy, and so he stood his ground. As he grew older he became more and more sure of his opinions and more outspoken. Yet at the same time he became more understanding and forgiving, and stressed the difficulty in making a decision. "Time is the grand revealer of all secrets ... the potent settler of all doubts."[9] Thus he strongly recommended that judgements be delayed until the accused could be observed over time by someone skilled. He continued: "If the law could exactly define the DEGREE of mental unsoundness which is compatible with full moral responsibility, a very great difficulty would be removed from the process of its administration ... I should hesitate to say that every degree or form of mental defect ... should exempt its subject from responsibility of his evil acts."[10]

Not all his detective cases involved murder. The first case on record, one involving impersonation, occurred when Joseph was Chairman of the Board of Education. A young teacher wrote to him appealing her dismissal. The letter was badly written and that made him suspicious, so he investigated further. He wrote to her wealthy Aunt Maud in Winnipeg requesting "a photo for a newspaper." The aunt sent back a photo of a cute little five-year-old. Refusing to be stymied, Joseph decided to brazen it out. When confronted, the young girl admitted to being a milliner's clerk. Her wealthy friend, the real teacher, had been struck dead by lightning, so she had risked the impersonation in order to collect Aunt Maud's generous monthly allowance, as well as the teacher's salary. She had changed from tutoring to classroom teaching in order to avoid detection.[11]

Joseph's weather journals came in useful on one occasion. The accused in question described the night of the murder as one disturbed by thunder and lightning, but Joseph's weather journal proved the man to be a liar.[12] Another case was a situation brought to him by a friend, Dr. Howlett, who suspected but could not prove fraud. The bookseller claimed the manuscript to be Elizabethan and worth a high price. At a glance Joseph declared it to be a fake. Most of the language suggested early Shakespeare, possibly an early draft of *Henry VI, Part I*, but the word "ungalvanized" was used in the text. Galvanizing was discovered in the eighteenth century, long after Shakespeare's death, indicating that the document was a clever fake. Joseph offered to buy the article for a few pounds, as an oddity. When the bookseller agreed, Joseph saw this as a confirmation of his opinion. Otherwise the man "would not so eagerly part with it for so paultry a sum as offered ... Whether the forgery was attempted in the eighteenth century, when some men tried to write 'new plays' by Shakespeare, or more recently, to hoodwink a gullible public, is the only question of doubt."[13]

One interesting case made headline news, and created fierce public debate. The Mary Boyd case involved a doctor, his ambitious wife, their adolescent son who was a medical student, and their pretty housemaid who claimed she was pregnant. People wondered what sort of guilt had induced her to commit suicide. She was an intelligent, modest, gentle, and attractive girl, who had taught Sunday School in the revivalist Presbyterian church in Eldon Township. Dr. Campbell, who treated her, said she was infatuated with the son and dreamed of intercourse with him. The doctor also said she had had menstrual difficulties but was not pregnant. Yet the instrument used by Dr. Campbell was, according to Joseph, used for abortions, not to encourage menstruation. Mary Boyd first tried to drown herself, saying it was better to be dead than alive. After she was rescued but before she could be certified, she attempted to sever her windpipe but did not manage to kill herself. At the Asylum two nurses tried to get her to talk. This caused the opening of the wound and she died. Joseph raised the following questions: Were the parents of the young man against their son marrying their housemaid? Was she really the housemaid? Did her former employer, a fire and brimstone preacher, create such guilt within her, that she claimed her own life? Why did her own father not visit her? On May 8, 1868, the jury censured Dr. Campbell for providing highly improper treatment, but reached no definite conclusions regarding why Mary wished to die. Joseph thought Mary Boyd was suffering from religious and sexual delusions, compounded by depression, but he was unable to fathom the riddle completely.[14] It seemed likely that the girl was pregnant and overwhelmed by the situation.

Exorcism was not officially practised by the Catholic Church at that time, but the uneducated still believed in it. Joseph described the case of a young nurse officially engaged to a labourer. She later changed her mind when she fell in love with another man, but for some reason the labourer would not let her break the engagement. He was found dead and Joseph was called in to perform the post-mortem. The strange circumstances made him suspicious, for the man seemed to have choked to death on a strange mixture of garlic buds, and the door was locked from the inside. There was another mixture of feces and garlic on the window-sill. Murder was suspected. Joseph, however, recognized the signs of a pagan exorcism, for he knew that garlic was supposed to offer protection against vampires. He decided the man had choked to death, but with provocation. He suspected that the young nurse and her new admirer had planted fear of vampires in the mind of the rather naive labourer, who then tried to carry out his own exorcism, dying in the attempt. Soon afterwards the nurse married the admirer, confirming Joseph's suspicions. Six years later the husband came to see Joseph, concerned that he was unable to produce children because of his "sexual problems." Joseph omitted any details but reported that he was able to help the man produce a large family. Possibly Joseph relieved him of his guilt and performed the first sex therapy recorded at the Toronto Asylum.[15]

Toronto had no documented witch burning such as Salem, Massachusetts. Joseph, nevertheless, was interested in the early theories of demon possession, and the vampires and witch burning associated with it. In 1871 he gave a speech to his colleagues on the topic, entitled "Demonomania and Witchcraft," in which he was very critical of the Scots led by James VI (James I of England) and of "Butcher Cromwell" in England, who had burned many witches at the stake. In his speech he also raised the issue of the gullible divines in seventeenth century Massachusetts who believed the allegations of their colleague, the Rev. Parris. As has been described in Arthur Miller's play, *The Crucible*, this minister used his servants and a troop of young girls to declare that his critics were "possessed." They were believed.

Joseph decided that these beliefs were still common amongst the less educated segments of society, especially where "fulminating pulpit orators" held sway. He felt these ideas were connected to the spiritualism popular in the late nineteenth century, which he called "mental darkness and puerile credulity." As a result he stressed the importance of early training during the formative years when people's beliefs, morals and intellectual character were being moulded. He believed many of the so-called witches and demon-possessed were really insane, and added that "the omnipotence of kindness" had cured far more than cruelty had ever done.[16]

Joseph wrote to his American friend, Dr. Jarvis, on July 18, 1871, saying he was disappointed at the response to the above mentioned speech which had been given to the American Superintendents at their annual meeting in Toronto. He had hoped for guidance from his colleagues on how to handle these superstitions at the Asylum. He was particularly incensed by the response of a Dr. Gundrie who, out of all the important issues he could have raised, made an "appeal to me as a Unitarian, in mitigation of Butcher Cromwell's superstition." Dr. Gundrie had suggested that Joseph should be sympathetic to the Puritan tradition of Massachusetts and to Cromwell's belief in witches, because the Unitarian tradition had grown out of the new religious freedom introduced by Cromwell, which had also blossomed in New England.

Another interesting case, that of Mary Ward, was the focus of a consultation Joseph gave after his retirement. Mary, the wife, died in a fire, with severe and strangely located burns. Her husband, a butcher, was less severely burnt and had survived. Curiously all his burns were on the left side of his body. Nearby lived a fifteen-year-old maid in whom the butcher seemed interested, and her rich father was offering a big dowry. As a result of all these facts, Joseph advised the consulting Dr. Murray that he suspected murder by the husband. The man was finally convicted, but not hanged. Joseph wrote in his case note: "Murray asked my opinion as to the man's sanity. I stated that to commit murder, especially premeditated, implies a certain kind of unsoundness of mind. To burn one's own flesh was not a rational act. As to actual sanity, there is a fine line between those we label and ourselves."[17]

Whether it was in searching out a diagnosis in a case of mental illness or finding the cause of death, Joseph used the same analysis of detail. Comments spoken in 1858 ring true for his work of the late seventies: "The advancement of sound pathological science, in the present day, depends perhaps more on the careful consideration, and proper application, of existing, simple facts, than on the discovery of additional or complex ones. We may spend much time in search of great truths which ultimately we may find have all the while been at our fingers."[18]

Behind these tales of Joseph as a nineteenth century sleuth, lies a modern story. In 1978 and 1979 the medical residents at the Queen Street Mental Health Centre became very interested in Dr. Workman. They voted to name the new auditorium in his honour, researched all the above incidents, and placed quotations from his speeches in their newsletter, *Matrix*. Ray Havelock, the Public Relations Officer at that time, noticed that they could identify with many of the things Joseph was saying, especially his resentment of government interference and cut-backs.

Joseph never seemed to lose his interest in training young clinicians and medical students. Two of his speeches to students dated 1883 have survived. In the Montreal Address, given at McGill University, he empathized with all the work they had to accomplish: "(You) students cannot possibly have time for shaving, darning your socks, or sparking. Some may have obliging cousins – you know what I mean – who will close up the breeches of continuity in your pedal envelopes, and in all probability you will conserve your hirsute appendages, as the fair sex seem to favour this caprous variety of the genus homo." Then he encouraged patience and skill in "unconscious celebration" while waiting for patients. His final advice was to cultivate "modesty," that is, an awareness that they always have more to learn.[19]

In the Toronto Address to the medical students, Joseph was more political. First he described the scenes he encountered at or near the Asylum in 1853: the farms, gardens and taverns; and the cesspool under the basement floor. Next he added in his usual potshots at politicians: "I recall an article in the *Globe* ... It said that there were three asylums within three miles of each other. Queen Street was the largest. From it people sometimes emerged with a whole mind. From the other two, no one ever emerged sound in mind, they were the Legislature and the City Hall ... Sir John A. said he encouraged building a hospital as a place to house Grits, so they need not roam the countryside unattended ... There were men then, there are in every age, who every time they spoke the sum total of human knowledge was greatly diminished. These men tried to run this hospital on a pittance. I railed against them. I fought them. For twenty-two years."[20]

Joseph next made fun of patronizing citizens: "Toronto the good! City of churches, twenty-two to be exact. Its citizens would pack a picnic lunch and come to gaze on the misfortunes of others and be amused. They'd laugh and point at the sick and chortle at bizarre behaviour. Enlightened, civilized, Christian Toronto. That was sickness all right."

Then he ended on a serious note: "You young people are sailing uncharted waters. You'll navigate new courses in unfamiliar streams, meet many dead ends, become grounded on sandbars of public ignorance, becalmed by lack of funds for your research, and suffer many a gale. The less hardy will abandon ship. The brave may yet reach the distant shore where sits understanding of these sicknesses, waiting to greet the fearless sailors of the deep, troubled waters of madness ... It is too easy to forget that the ends we serve are not our careers, to rise in our profession and receive accolades from our peers, but humanity. If we are no better than pedlars seeking profit, albeit in honours not dollars, then we should leave medicine.

"The easiest thing to do is to lock the insane in cells and feed them and forget them. The hardest is to find that spark of humanity that dwells in each of us. We all are tempted to quit the race at one time or another. But, as was said so very long ago, the race is not to the swift. No, it is to he who perseveres. I pass the torch to you. Carry it proudly to Olympus itself. God speed and goodbye."

CHAPTER THIRTEEN

Honours
(1875-1894)

*"I wish I could feel that I truly deserve all the praises that
have been bestowed on me."*
J.W.

IN retirement honours began to arrive, combined with recognition
of his skills. In 1876 Joseph became President of the Canadian Institute. The next year he took on the Presidency of the Canadian
Medical Association, which he had helped found back in 1867. The
year after that he became an honorary member and the first President of the Toronto Medical Society, a reorganization of the
Medico-Chirurgical Society of Upper Canada. He declined a third
term in 1880. In 1881 he founded and was first President of the
Ontario Medical Association. To add to that he became an honorary member of the Boston Gynaecological Society and in 1882, the
Montreal Medical Society. He received an award from the
Phreniatic Society of Italy, who appreciated his many translations
of their work for the English speaking world. He also received an
award from the Medico Psychological Society of Great Britain and
Ireland, an award that no one else in North America had ever received. Despite all these accolades Joseph still treated his colleagues
to his sardonic humour. After the June 1881 meeting of the Ontario Medical Association he wrote that 127 members were present
"of which ninety-two paid their fees." Of the death of the
Chirurgical society he commented that it "fell victim to slop milk
and colloquial diarrhea."[1]

When, however, the medical profession was under attack, Joseph was not hesitant to defend its reputation. A letter written in 1868 to an Irish doctor in Stratford, named John Galbraith Hyde, illustrates his attitude. He encouraged the Stratford doctor to appeal a malpractice suit which he felt was based primarily on professional animosity, and Hyde later did this successfully. At that time Joseph expresses his feelings in a letter to Dr. Hyde: "I am proud to learn that you think Doctors better the Lawyers – I have often felt ashamed of the meanness and the ignorance of many of our body; but of many, perhaps the majority – I have a high opinion; and I thank you for corroborating it – Very truly and undisturbedly, Yours, Workman.[2]

In addition to his other tasks and despite his age, during the early 1880s Joseph became a consulting physician at the Homewood Retreat, a private sanitarium founded by Langmuir, the Inspector, and run by a Dr. Stephen Lett. This was a new experiment for inebriates and the mentally ill. Joseph was even the Interim Medical Superintendent when Dr. Lett was away. In later years Joseph's son, Fred, recuperated at Homewood (see the next chapter regarding Fred). Joseph's energy at this stage in his life was remarkable.

After all the honours had been showered on him, Joseph received a jolt in 1884 when he heard that Dr. Tuke had been informed that he, Joseph, had left the Asylum in a disgraceful condition. In characteristic fashion he immediately acted to rectify that impression. He wrote to his old friend and colleague, Inspector Langmuir, who sent him a testimonial by return mail. Another very flattering testimonial arrived from E. A. Meridith, LL.D., Chairman of the Board of Inspectors from 1859 to 1869.[3] Joseph was very happy with these assessments and sent them to Dr. Tuke. He was proud of the work which had consumed so much of his life, and was not hesitant to say so.

In December 1888 an oil portrait of Joseph was completed by a J. W. L. Forster from a photo taken in 1878 by Common of Elora. On Christmas Eve Joseph wrote in his diary that there were "glowing eulogies" when it was unveiled. The portrait was hung in the

Toronto Medical Society Library, and now graces the new Toronto Hospital Boardroom. In 1890 a bust of Joseph by a Mr. F. Dunbar was completed. In his diary (July 31) he complained bitterly of having spent forty-five hours sitting for it. Yet he bought four copies! The original at the Toronto Medical Library was given recently to the Queen Street Mental Health Centre, and copies are found at the First Unitarian Congregation and at the Toronto Board of Education. A skilled descendant (Nellie Baker) even created a smaller version, and copies are popular with family members.

In 1892, when Joseph began visibly to age and his hand started to shake following a mild paralytic stroke, his many friends and colleagues decided to celebrate his eighty-seventh birthday. They had hoped that he might reach a hundred and two like his mother, but the signs were otherwise. Eighty letters and many greetings arrived from the medical profession, including former students, from family, from Unitarians and from politicians.[4] Several are included in the appendix. Joseph wrote in his diary on May 26: "I wish I could feel that I truly deserve all the praises that have been bestowed on me."

One of the writers, Dr. Charles K. Clarke, gave a very moving testimonial: "Personally I have always felt that one of the brightest spots in my life has been my friendship with you, and I thoroughly appreciate the advantage that it has been to have had the benefit of your advice and direction. It must be a satisfaction to you to know that all young men who have fallen under your inspiration have been encouraged in a manner that has made their lives purer and better. Yours has been an ideal life and those of us who love you best would express the admiration we feel. You have not lived in vain, but have achieved the highest ideal a man can strive for, that of having existed, not for the glorification of himself, but for the happiness of others. There are few of us perhaps who fully understand what your influence on asylum management has been in Ontario. Is not the undying gratitude of a suffering humanity far more grateful than the loud sounding applause of a thoughtless multitude. I know that in my work the precepts and examples laid down by you, come home to me with peculiar force almost every hour, and when I allow them to act as guiding stars I never go astray. Those of us still alive are as a unit in our regard for the good old man who has been a father to them."

Richard Maurice Bucke seemed surprised at Joseph's age. He too held Joseph in high regard, and wrote: "Many years have you lived the honoured chief in our chosen country of our common specialty; and many more may you live as you are today, the most learned and the most able of Canadian Alienists. I am, dear Dr. Workman, your friend and admirer."

Oliver Wendell Holmes, Justice of the US Supreme Court and a one time Unitarian, wrote: "Though I know you only by your high reputation, I venture to count among the friends who congratulate you."

Daniel Lamb, a longterm Unitarian and alderman of the city stressed: "I greatly value the friendship which has descended from my Father and Mother of fifty years duration." Thomas Joseph Workman Burgess, his former student and son of another longterm Unitarian friend, had similar warm feelings.

His daughter-in-law, Jane Clarke Workman, focused on the fact that "joys and sorrows have come strangely often to the family in this season of blossoms." His granddaughter, Bessie Workman, told him of the box of flowers sent to him from Stratford. She remembered the birthday greetings only when she reached the postscript. Her other grandfather, Colonel Clarke, reminisced about the forty years of friendship, and how Joseph had placed his experience so freely at Clarke's disposal.

These are only a taste of the heart warming tributes he received!

CHAPTER FOURTEEN

Family Ties

*"I have great reason to be thankful to a Gracious Providence for
many blessings, among which has been that of a tender,
loving wife and good children."*
J.W.

"ALL the Workman brothers are very independent of each other;
no hugging ever," declared Charles Dall, the Unitarian minister in
Toronto, in 1852 to his colleague in Montreal.[1] Dall would be think-
ing of Joseph, from his own congregation, but the minister of the
Montreal church would be thinking of Thomas, William and Ben.
To both ministers the Workman brothers were formidable figures.

Before exploring individual differences in the brothers, a look
at the parents might be helpful. Despite Ben's complimentary comments about his parents (see Chapter Two), his diary also reveals them
to be tough, strict and self-disciplined. The father did not cease when
at home to be the school teacher. He clearly was frustrated with Ben's
resistance to following a business career, but he seemed able to cope
with the stubborn lad. In his heart of hearts he must have admired the
boy's determination. According to Ben, his father's heart swelled with
pride when Ben wrote to say he was in charge of a private establishment in the city of Montreal, not just teaching in a rural school.

Catharine, the mother, is a more shadowy figure. She was an intelligent young woman and a bright student who married a man ten
years older than herself, which was not unusual in those days. She
enjoyed excellent health and abundant energy, and was held in high
repute for her hospitality. She was ambitious for her children, and
alleged to be one of the driving forces behind them. She was admired

by her children and Joseph called her "his best friend."[2] He commented in his personal diary that she kept her intellectual faculties right up to the end. She was a caring person, who kept contact with her large extended family. In a letter sent in 1866 to her grandson, William, in Stratford, she signed it with an interesting twist, "Your affectionate grandmother to death." Yet a harsher picture is given by Ben's daughter, Annie, who grew up with her grandmother. According to her descendants, Annie was seldom hugged by her grandmother. The only cuddling she received was from the maids, and furthermore, her grandmother did not allow her downstairs because they were now "upper crust." Nor was she taught how to cook or shop, a lack that her husband, Dr. Joseph Bascom of Uxbridge, rectified by doing the shopping himself and by arranging cooking lessons for her. This picture of Catharine Workman corresponds in some respects to Ben's picture of his father. The Workman parents seemed stricter and more class conscious than either Ben or Joseph. They were products of a puritan age, when physical affection (which was seen as spoiling the child) was frowned on, at least by the middle classes in the British Isles. Their lack of hugging was considered very unusual by the American Unitarians in Montreal.

The Unitarian Congregation in Montreal tended to attract independent and ambitious businessmen who seemed to relish a cool austerity and aloofness. Such a man was Thomas Workman, Joseph's favourite younger brother. The minister who officiated at his funeral was an American, William Barnes, who felt obliged to remark on it: "He was one of Montreal's merchant princes. Some have the impression that he was not a man of emotions," but the minister went on to say that he had at times glimpsed a more tender side.[3] Joseph certainly saw the more tender side for he wrote in his diary on February 23, 1889, that he believed Thomas died of a broken heart, following the death of his wife. It was Thomas to whom Joseph turned when he needed to borrow money in 1852, and again in 1867, to buy a Stratford hardware business for his sons. It was at Thomas's home he stayed when visiting Montreal, and Thomas also visited him occasionally at the Asylum. They shared many interests including the study of evolution and the works of Darwin.

Thomas became the richest of all the brothers. (See the Appendix for the family tree.) He moved from being a senior partner in Frothingham and Workman Hardware to President of the Molson's Bank, and then first President of the Sun Life Insurance Company and a Director of Canada Shipping. He became a millionaire, donating generously to good causes, including a quarter to a half million dollars given (over time) to McGill University, and smaller sums to provide free libraries. In the momentous year of 1867 he was elected as a Liberal from Montreal Centre to the House of Commons and re-elected in 1875. Unitarianism and the minister, the Rev. John Cordner, always received his firmest support, and indeed he even had his own private Unitarian chapel built in his home. When he died he donated his home to McGill, his house becoming the Music Department.

William also remained in Montreal, and became very wealthy. He speculated in railways, steamships, real estate and banking. He also showed concern for the less fortunate, establishing several Benevolent Societies, a Savings Bank for Working Men, and better urban sanitation. Unlike his brothers, he supported the Conservatives and Sir John A. Macdonald, and accused Thomas and the Liberals of being scented with a "spice of communism!"[4] Finally in 1868 he too received political recognition, becoming a very popular Mayor of Montreal for three years. This helped to compensate for the death of four of his six children, the most heartbreaking of which was the loss of his only son. That same year he sought comfort in visiting a leading phrenologist in the States, hoping to read the future from the bumps on his head. He ended his visit by seeing the murdered body of Abraham Lincoln. Joseph was not very fond of William, and commented in his diary that he had always maintained that William had damage inside his head as well as the bumps outside. On February 24, 1878, he wrote: "My red cross marks are but too well understood by all our scandalised family ... (Anna and niece have the items so marked) ... Seldom has the poverty of riches been more piteously exemplified than in the life and death of this unhappy man. He could never tolerate honest friends who dared disapprove of his conduct ... his mental constitution was abnormal. His ultimate cerebral and spinal impairment must be regarded as corroboration of this opinion."

William had his own battle with the Montreal minister, John Cordner. The story goes that he was late for church, and the heavy country shoes which he loved to wear squeaked loudly as he entered. This was repeated the following week, so Cordner stopped the service and rebuked him from the pulpit. William walked out, never to return. As a result he then built his own private chapel but, unlike Thomas, this one was "for spite."[5]

Alexander, the second oldest brother, finally settled in the hardware business in Ottawa with his foster brother from Ireland named Edward Griffin, and Edward's sister, Elizabeth. They did well financially. Alexander became School Superintendent for a while, a Board of Education Trustee for twenty years, and finally became Mayor of Ottawa in 1859. He met the Prince of Wales, and assisted in laying the corner stone of the present Parliament buildings. In vain he tried to start a Unitarian Congregation, but finally settled in fairly happily at St. Paul's Presbyterian. As his one and only son died young, he befriended Joseph's son, Thomas, who spent most of his life in Ottawa and inherited his hardware business. Joseph does not say much about Alexander, but seemed fond of him.

Samuel seemed the quiet brother. He came to help Joseph run the business in Toronto in the 1840s, and became Treasurer of the church, but later he returned to Montreal with his family, and lived next door to his widowed mother. Unfortunately he was paralysed for the final nineteen years of his life (1850-1869). He did not achieve fame or fortune, the only surviving brother not to do so.

Joseph sent him and his mother money in their later years.

The one sister, Ann, settled in Montreal, and married a Henry Mulholland who also managed a hardware store, Mulholland and Baker. Joseph and Elizabeth kept in close touch, sending their two oldest sons, William and Fred, to live with the Mulhollands in the mid 1850s in order to learn the business. The boys remained there for several years.

Joseph did not record his feelings about Ben. Initially, perhaps, he was too close to him to risk offending him, or perhaps he just found it hard to put his feelings into words. Even at Ben's death he seemed speechless, an unusual situation for Joseph. The fact that they managed to work together for nineteen years speaks for itself. There was a deep mutual respect. Ben was certainly loved by the staff at the Toronto Asylum, and in parting he was given a beautiful parchment signed by nearly one hundred employees, "as a token expression of our esteem and respect (for your) kindness and attention."[6]

Elizabeth played the role of a traditional, caring but passive wife, who appeared content to live at the Asylum. She enjoyed her children, sewing, growing flowers, and visiting friends and relations. Certainly by living in the very centre of the administration tower, she was never very far away from the action. One of her letters written to their son, William, in 1854, reveals some interesting comments: "I have never had so little to do ... I have four servants, and can have as many more as I wish, patients I mean; there are several wish to live with me ... Rosie, a patient, ... is with me ... she would die with fright if put in the wards. She never speaks but to me. She can do everything we tell her and well too. She says she is always afraid of being killed.

"Lines (are) put up every night on the verandas, to hang the patients' clothes on as they take them off ... they used to leave them in bundles at the room doors and the perspiration on them would almost make one sick passing them ... All the patients are getting as much meat as they can eat at least once a day; some of them used not to have half enough; there is great improvement in their health and appearance. I think they could not have got a better Superintendent for he spends his whole time for the benefit of the Institution and never thinks it is half well enough."[7]

Joseph wrote an interesting comment in 1835, the year he was married, and one wonders if this was his picture of Elizabeth. He advocated that a recovering cholera patient hire a male attendant, preferably not family, because women were not to be trusted. "They have not sufficient firmness, or rather they are possessed of too much tenderness to resist the almost irresistible entreaties which the patient often makes, of something to satiate his unquenchable thirst ... So far as courage is concerned, to encounter the greatest personal danger, and affection, to undergo the most trying privations, our confidence in them may be unlimited, they never desert their post. Men are cowards by the bedside of pestilence, but women seem to acquire energies beyond the powers of our conception."[8]

Joseph did not reveal much directly about his wife, except that she was "a tender, loving wife." His personal diary has lots of small affectionate comments, especially after her death on May 16, 1885, two weeks before their fiftieth wedding anniversary. On that occasion he wrote at length about his loss, quoting two stanzas from a poem entitled "There is a Charm in the Past." Indeed, the last entry in his diary, written on May 16, 1893, in his own shaky hand, was a tribute to Elizabeth. He regularly visited her grave and was buried beside her in the Toronto Necropolis, as were several of their children. (The three infants originally buried in Potter's Field were reburied in the family grave.) An attractive memorial records their lives. As his daughter-in-law, Jane Clarke, said in 1892, many personal events happened to Joseph in blossom time. May 25 had been his graduation, May 26 was his birthday, May 30 was their wedding anniversary, and finally May 16 was the date of his loss of Elizabeth.

Elizabeth gave birth to ten children, four of whom died before reaching two years of age (two of dysentery, one of cholera and Catharine of scarlet fever and croup). The loss of four infants must have depressed both parents as well as the remaining children. These events were accepted with fortitude for child mortality was common at that time, but it would have been especially hard for Elizabeth, whose life revolved around the children. Joseph probably escaped into work and into his books.

Most of Joseph's children did not lead a normal life, being raised as they were for many years on the Asylum premises, that is, all except the oldest two who were sent to the Mulhollands in Montreal. The children's feelings on the subject have not been recorded. Joseph was able to inspire students to enter psychiatry, but he did not seem able to inspire his own sons. One of his younger boys, Joseph, attended Upper Canada College and the University of Toronto, and then tried out for a time as a resident at the Asylum. But he left abruptly three days before Christmas 1874, following a period of illness. Surprisingly, Joseph made no personal comment in his diary beside the entry. The young man went to join his brothers in the Stratford hardware business. Many observers of celebrities have pointed out that it is very difficult for the son or daughter of a famous person to establish their own identity. They are torn between following in the father's footsteps, and branching out on their own. In addition, high achievers can be very critical of their own offspring. The boys saw their father as kind but they also observed his high standards and his ability to be sarcastic. Whatever the cause, none of them were inspired to spend their lives helping the mentally ill. The oldest boys chose instead to follow the example of their father which they had observed in their earliest childhood, the more tangible hardware business.

The connotations in Joseph's diary seldom betrayed his normally well-controlled emotions. When he wrote about his sons, it was most frequently about their finances. He was sure they would not be frugal if he was too generous. Despite generously buying the hardware business in Stratford for William and Fred, he kept them on a tight budget and was constantly giving them advice. Money was also used to control other members of the family. For example, he wrote to his daughter-in-law, Jane Clarke Workman, offering a financial gift ($100) if they named their first daughter Elizabeth after her mother-in-law. Later he offered another bribe to name a second granddaughter after his mother. He commented that he had one grand-daughter, Katherine, but she was named after another. He wished a Catharine, and he got his wish.

It is of interest that Joseph donated to the medical education of a friend's child, namely Susanna Boyle, daughter of David Boyle. Joseph wrote in his will that he appreciated "her mental endowments and her moral worth." (She was one of the few female pioneers going into medicine at that time.) Perhaps she, in addition to C. K. Clarke and Thomas Burgess, were the ones to inherit Joseph's enthusiasm about medicine rather than his own children.

Joseph's two girls seemed able to access the gentler and more tender aspect of his personality, at least this is the impression given in his diary. Florence did not marry and remained at home to help. She was described as warm, witty and very popular. A family record mentioned that Colonel Clarke was interested in marrying her, following the death of his first wife, but she declined. She frequently escorted Joseph on outings, especially in his old age. After his death she became the volunteer Treasurer of the National Humane Society.

Anna married one of the brilliant, handsome but rather unstable, clinical assistants at the Asylum, a Dr. John E. Kennedy, on July 30, 1870, in St. John's Church. (It is of note that it was not at the Unitarian Church.) This event elicited more emotion from Joseph than any other in his diary. Anna had chosen another strong-willed doctor, who resisted Joseph's control. First, Joseph had misgivings when Uncle Thomas showered them with very expensive gifts. Next, Joseph complained in his diary that "the wedding fooleries" cost him ten times what his own wedding cost ($350 as compared to $35). He added: "Our children live in another age and know little of the penury passed through by their parents." Joseph revealed that he had offered the groom $50 "to avoid the sail" to Montreal, this "Marriage Tour" being the current fad for honeymooners. The groom had returned the money, "as he expected to be able to support his wife when he would be married." Joseph was angry at the words and tone of the letter. He continued: "(Anna) has been a very good and dutiful child. I never raised a finger in correction of her in her life and I do not remember ever to have had to reprove her. May God bless her." Then in August he wrote that he intended to send her the rent money from one of his houses as a regular present (about $200 a year). In November he sent her a piano. It is surprising that he did not see how this would upset the proud Dr. Kennedy, or perhaps he did it to aggravate him. One wonders if he believed he was helping Anna survive. It seems he was caught in a power struggle with his son-in-law, as in a Freudian drama.

Dr. Kennedy did well in the profession and became a Professor of Therapeutics at Trinity Medical School and a lecturer in Venereal Diseases at the Toronto General Hospital. He became famous for his delicate bowel by-pass operations, with patients coming from all over North America and occasionally Europe. He worked long hours and was under much stress. About once a year or so, he cracked and went on a drinking binge, when he might spend days away from home or collapse on the sofa in a drunken stupor.[9] So life was sometimes very difficult for Anna.

During the hot summer of 1872 Anna brought her one-year-old daughter and her nurse to stay at the cooler Asylum for two months. The child blossomed. Two years later Anna brought little Katherine, nicknamed Kitty, who was in a "dying state." Joseph nursed her back to health over the course of two months, for which Anna was eternally grateful. Joseph was delighted to have them around, and commented that Dr. Kennedy's loss was his gain. Earlier that year, on March 7, Joseph had bought Anna a house on John Street for his "daughter's comfort," commenting that it felt like a poor investment "until Dr. Kennedy feels disposed to take the purchase into his own hands." Anna must have had split loyalties but she did not separate from her husband. Dr. Kennedy died in 1891, at a relatively young age. Joseph agreed to have the funeral at his home on Mutual Street to please Anna but refused to attend. He was reputed to have commented that he would rather go to the death of a dog. Anna lived on until 1922. Kitty married Cecil Lavell (Lavelle), the brother of the warden at Kingston Penitentiary, and nephew of one of the past ministers of the Toronto Unitarian Ccongregation. (Kitty inherited Joseph's weather diaries, which the Lavelle family donated in 1922 to the Meteorological Service of Canada. See Chapter Eleven.)

In his annual report of 1873 Joseph commented on marriage: "As far as liability to insanity is concerned, marriage is very dangerous to women, and single life very dangerous to men, while married men and single women enjoy comparative immunity." This is an observation that has been repeated by researchers in recent years. Perhaps Joseph was thinking of his own children!

The Workman family had been blessed with high intelligence and generally good health, but one scourge seemed to plague them, the problem of alcoholism. Joseph's uncle Benjamin, the gifted teacher who had gone to America with his father, had returned later to Ireland and had become an alcoholic in his senior years, according to Dr. Ben's diary. That was probably one reason Dr. Ben was so involved with the temperance movement. The problem did not stop with that generation. Two of Elizabeth Wasnidge's four brothers died young of "liver complaints" when only 29 and 36. Indeed at the funeral of the latter, Alfred Wasnidge, in 1853, the Unitarian minister, Charles Dall, noted "intemperance" as the cause of death. The Workman family records suggest that two of Joseph's brothers, William and Samuel, had a problem with alcohol. Certainly the problem struck again with Joseph's oldest two sons, especially Fred. As a boy Fred had chronically poor health, which concerned the family and even the staff and patients, who were reported to be very fond of him. Joseph would only write in his diary that Fred was "sick again," and was returning to the Asylum to "recover his strength." He probably realized that he and Elizabeth had passed along a genetic predisposition. That may have been why he held onto the purse strings so tightly. William and Fred must have had mixed feelings, resenting their father's ongoing control, yet grateful for the hardware business and his support. They were aware that their father had borrowed the money from their Uncle Thomas, in order to give them a start in life.

William settled down in later years and at aged forty married the twenty-three year old Jane Clarke, C. K. Clarke's sister and daughter of Colonel Charles Clarke, the very close friend of his father. Joseph was very fond of "Miss Jennie" and had helped arrange the match. William then fathered eight children, the youngest daughter inheriting the longevity gene from her namesake, Catharine Gowdey Workman, her great-grandmother. William had taught at the Unitarian Sunday School in Montreal but now attended the Anglican Church in Stratford with his wife. He became a respectable and well-liked businessman, and even followed in his father's footsteps by becoming a school trustee and an expert on the natural world, in his case botany.[10]

His brothers, Fred and Joseph, married two sisters, named Moderwell. Fred died relatively young at fifty, of meningitis. Joseph also had health problems, but his chronic bronchitis disappeared when he went to Colorado, where he settled down as a engineer in Walsenburg. Thomas went to his uncle's in Ottawa, and eventually inherited his hardware business.

In addition to raising their own six surviving children, Joseph and Elizabeth became the guardians of three others. Joseph left each of them money in his will. First was Lizzie Wasnidge, the daughter of Joseph Wasnidge, Elizabeth's last surviving brother, who had taken up an arduous career in farming, but had died young, possibly of "overwork" and "consumption (tuberculosis)."[11] He spent his final days in 1861 at the Asylum being nursed by the Workmans. His widow raised the three boys but Lizzie had a chronic health problem. The child came to the Asylum at the age of three for a visit and never left. She became a very elegant and well-educated lady who claimed she never had to learn housework skills. She married one of Joseph's medical residents and lived in one of Joseph's houses on Mutual Street. Her children reported that they much appreciated the money Joseph left her in his will.

The second child raised was John A. Scott, the child of a friend of Joseph Wasnidge. When the friend died the kind hearted Elizabeth offered to raise the boy.

The third child raised by the Workmans was Johnnie Heber McDougall, the grandson of Elizabeth's sister, Mary. Both his mother and his grandmother had died in childbirth, and his father, William McDougall, seemed indifferent to his welfare. Joseph later complained in his diary that the father never offered any support for the child. Joseph was by then (March 1871) sixty-six years old and Elizabeth fifty-eight, but they responded immediately to the cry for help. It is a touching story how Joseph brought the two-week-old infant back from Aurora on horseback, perched on the front of his saddle, a distance of about twenty miles. The Workmans were reported to spoil the baby, and the following quotation gives this credence.

In 1872 Joseph wrote a touching letter to "Miss Jennie," C. K. Clarke's sister, encouraging her to visit the Asylum to enjoy the babies: "All my spare time is devoted to the extermination of potato bugs, tile drains, ivy, and nursing Johnnie, to keep him from scratching Annie's Babbins, who, by the way, is a most sweet child, for Johnnie scratches her and wools her hair, just because he sees Pa likes her ... though when Johnnie is not present, Pa (that is Grandpa) does like to nurse Babbins, and hear her prattle. Sometimes Mister McDougall permits Babbins to sit on my left knee, whilst his Lordship sits on the right one – but poor Babbins is fond of kissing and being kissed – being of the softer sex – and this brings trouble, for Johnnie repudiates both kissing and being kissed. He calls the patients that say "kiss me, Johnnie," "cazywimmen" and orders them to "go away," but outside he will not even allow them to walk on the planks near Ba … He is well worth it all."[12] In retirement Joseph much enjoyed Johnnie and his grandchildren. He had more time and was more relaxed than when his own children were small.

A quick look at the marriages amongst the doctors in this narrative reveals that their social life must have been relatively restricted and so they chose marriage partners connected with their careers. For example, Anna married one of her father's clinical assistants, as mentioned earlier. Ben's daughter, Annie, married another assistant, Dr. Joseph Bascom. William married Jane Clarke ("Miss Jennie"), and her sister, Emma, married another of Joseph's interns, Dr. William Metcalf, the superintendent who was murdered at the Rockwood Criminal Asylum by a patient. Lizzie Wasnidge married yet another resident, Dr. Jonathan Robinson, later an Assistant at Rockwood. Thus the professional letters to each other contained much personal family information, for they had become like a large extended family.

Joseph passed away quietly on April 15, 1894. As revealed in his diary, Joseph seemed content at the time of his death. He felt he had done his duty, followed his religious and moral principles. He felt his children had all settled down finally, and were "good children." He was thankful to a "Gracious Providence" for a good life.[13]

In Retrospect

*"It is too easy to forget that the ends we serve is not our careers, to
rise in our profession and receive accolades from our peers, but
humanity. If we are no better than pedlars seeking profit, albeit
in honours not dollars, then we should leave medicine.
The easiest thing to do is to lock the insane in cells and feed them
and forget them. The hardest is to find that spark of humanity
that dwells in each of us. We all are tempted to quit the race
at one time or another. But, as was said so very long ago,
the race is not to the swift. No, it is to he who perseveres.
I pass the torch to you."*
J.W.

On the occasion of Joseph's 87th birthday, Dr. C. K. Clarke told him that he "had not lived in vain but had achieved the highest ideal a man could strive for ... the happiness of others ... and the undying gratitude of a suffering humanity." Dr. Clarke also stressed that Joseph had laid the groundwork of asylum reform for those, like himself, who followed, and had inspired them to carry "the torch" proudly. On another occasion he wrote: "Dr. Workman not only showed how terrible the tragedy of mental disease is but his wonderful sympathy and devotion taught a lesson never to be forgotten. Truly his was the life of a great man devoted to a great work. Even in the beginning of the shadow of old age, I look back with love and admiration on the work of the greatest man I have ever known."[1] In 1894, after Joseph's death he commented: "One of the most eminent alienists North America has had."[2]

As mentioned throughout this narrative, and especially in Chap-

ter Four, Joseph enjoyed being at the beginning of many new institutions, in their formative and flexible stages. He did this not only
in psychiatry, but in business, education, public health, liberal religion, medical training, and legislation related to mental illness. How
do we in the late twentieth century view Joseph's life, and his contributions to the building of our society? Is the title "Father of Canadian Psychiatry" appropriate and justified?

Before the century was over, Dr. Richard Maurice Bucke and
Dr. C. K. Clarke also built for themselves important reputations as
psychiatrists, but they built on Joseph's work. First, it is clear that
none of them were truly original. Joseph was not the first person to
bring "moral treatment" to Canada from Europe and England, but
he was first to develop, test and interpret these ideas over time in
the English Canadian environment. His administrative skills were
finely tuned, and he developed a model on which the rest could
build. Second, no further major revolution in psychiatry occurred
until Freud, Jung and the development of biochemistry. Finally,
Joseph realized that more refined scientific tools were necessary
to explore further. He was aware that many of the "causes" listed
in his era were only triggers, propelling over the brink into insanity, someone who already had a predisposition. He searched in vain
for other causes, but never gave up hope. In paving the way for
others to follow, he earned the title of "Father of Canadian Psychiatry."

In many respects Joseph was a nineteenth century "Renaissance
man," an intellectual with numerous and varied interests. He was
also ahead of his time, and with the right type of personality to
establish new ideas in the turbulent years of that century, for he
had the appropriate mix of self-confidence, political savvy, and professional knowledge to persuade, cajole, and implement the changes
needed. He had great tenacity of purpose and an exceedingly strong
belief in what he was doing, an arrogance according to some. When
he was knocked down, he had the drive to pick himself up and try

again. He could work long hours for months on end. Viewed through modern eyes, Joseph was certainly authoritarian and controlling, a tough and articulate foe when riled, and all in all a formidable presence. Yet he was also kind, patient, compassionate, generous, a man to emulate.

In American studies it is noted that the Irish Presbyterians who settled in North America (whom they call "Scots-Irish") were unusually hardworking, financially canny, with little time for the arts, yet with a great and exaggerated sense of humour, all of which helped them survive and prosper. Joseph fits this description.

Undoubtedly Joseph held a few mistaken ideas, (such as the then current view regarding masturbation), but on the whole it is remarkable how modern was his diagnostic approach to mental illness. For example, he recognized that his patients had a physical predisposition, set off by emotional and physical triggers. In his study of alcoholism he observed what we now call "fetal alcohol syndrome." He was very modern in many of his treatment programs, such the use of an outpatient system, the introduction of a "halfway house," and an emphasis on individualized medical and dental care as part of the total therapy. The focus on employment, fresh air, exercise, good food, kindness and honesty involves principles known today as occupational therapy and "milieu therapy," respectively. He also recognized the value of offering nothing more than good care, realizing that the body has its own recuperative mechanisms.

The introduction of internships with a residency training program was Joseph's idea and implemented at his insistence. He later read about a similar program in Italy, which encouraged him to publicize the idea in North America, but in vain. Only much later did others follow his example. His Asylum residents in Toronto, however, much appreciated the program and his interest in their careers. The devotion of C. K. Clarke, Thomas Burgess, and William Canniff was well recorded. Noteworthy too is the fact that he also was unusually popular and influential with the undergraduate medical students and with the newly trained doctors. He loved to impart his knowledge, and he knew how to do it with wit and humour, though occasionally his use of hyperbole upset his audience. Most of his colleagues also learned from and admired him, despite the occasional sarcasm which descended unexpectedly on their heads, for the comments seldom seemed to be personal, designed rather to liven up the meeting. He was noted for loyalty to his friends, refusing to have negative things said about them in his presence. He was able to build connections and friendships in high places, not only in Canada but also in the U.S.A. and in Europe (particularly Italy and of course Great Britain). On the other hand he had not forgotten his own modest beginnings. For example, he spent hours just talking to his patients, most of whom came from very humble circumstances. His warmth and patience were probably what endeared him to so many.

Another endearing quality was Joseph's loyalty to his wife, children and extended family members. One friend described Joseph as having a "blameless life."[4] It is likely that he was referring to the fact that no sexual gossip or financial scandal was ever attached to Joseph's name, not even by George Brown. Joseph was able (as far as we know) to live up to his own high moral code. He did his duty, an important value in those days, and "maintained his honour," another respected trait of the period. He lived according to his principles. For example, he must have been disappointed that none of his children followed him into medicine, but one of his principles was individual freedom of thought, which involved choice of action too. He accepted his sons' decisions without comment, or at least there was no criticism in his diary. (Perhaps he realized that his children would inherit the diaries!) But there are no letters on record discussing the subject, or his concern about their alcoholism. Only his sentimental feelings regarding his wife and daughters were allowed to show. In this he was a typical "Victorian," emotionally repressed and overly concerned with proper behaviour and self-discipline.

Joseph was very progressive for the time in his views about women's education and the women's vote (as exemplified in the Unitarian constitution). He talked about teaching people to think through issues for themselves. Yet the women in his life seemed to live very traditional roles and were described by him as "tender, loving and good." Their education and their opinions were seldom mentioned. Joseph's practice lagged behind the theory, as is frequently the case with pioneering thinkers. The mores of the society around them exerted a more powerful influence on the Workman women than the father's theoretical principles. In addition, as with the boys, Joseph's personality was so strong and dominant that they were probably intimidated. He read so many books, and spoke so many languages. He may have been humble about his ignorance, but he was self-confident about his knowledge. Indeed his many interests and his grasp of so many topics must have overwhelmed most people.

Joseph certainly believed in God, as interpreted through Jesus, but he had a liberal interpretation of the New Testament, which did not include the tenets of the Westminster confession. In this regard he remained true to the religion of his childhood. He criticized those he considered fanatical and judgemental, those who preached hell and damnation, for he thought religious teaching should guide, console, inspire, and stress God's grace and pardon. He displayed considerable courage to admit to being a Unitarian in an age when religious persecution was prevalent. His affiliation must have been widely known; certainly, the American Asylum Superintendents were aware of it.

His moral code and sense of duty were interwoven with principles of democracy and fair play, some of which were typical Liberal Reform but others seemed influenced by the American experience and values of his father. Regarding the democratic vote, he wrote: "The minority cannot, as indeed they should not, in a free country, impose laws on an adverse majority: and as, in our system of representative government, we must hold that the will of the majority is right, and is the supreme sanction of our laws."[5] Back in his days as an alderman, he had fought for a Freedom of Elections bill, designed to stop those with vested interests from making the decisions.

Not only did Joseph believe in democracy and a social conscience, but he stressed putting them into action and building the public institutions and services necessary to help the poor, the sick, the immigrant, the mentally ill as well as the average citizen. He observed the connection between poverty and ill health, and advocated that these services be publicly supported and carefully supervised by trained personnel. In his later years it was interference by "untrained" politicians that he decried, for his experiences at the Asylum had turned him against politicians. In his speech to the American Superintendents on the topic of asylum management, he said it was actually a "valuable civil boon" for superintendents to be discouraged from "exercising electoral franchise;" that is to say, a certain detachment from the political scene had become advantageous, especially when stability of tenure was paramount in asylum management. Yet in many ways Joseph owed his success to his political astuteness and certainly to his affiliation with the Liberal Reform Party in the mid-nineteenth century.

Joseph was not a strong nationalist, supporting the constitutional monarchy yet swayed by the teachings of Franklin, Jefferson and Washington. Indeed, the American medical journals recognized him as one of their own and called him the "Nestor of students of mental disease."[7] He believed in free trade with the United States, and would have been quite happy if Canada had joined the U.S.A. So in that sense he is not a good Canadian hero. But times have changed and he might have thought differently today.

Despite all these achievements and contributions to our society, Joseph is nearly forgotten in the late twentieth century. Yet not completely. His portrait adorns the new boardroom of the Toronto Hospital. His bust greets the visitor to the Queen Street Mental Health Centre, and their auditorium is named after him. The First Unitarian Congregation of Toronto have displayed his bust in a place of honour and have a hall named after him and Ben. Their annual Workman Lecture has been ongoing since 1965, with celebrated speakers from across Canada, the U.S.A., and Northern Ireland. The Toronto Board of Education (1850-1998) has his name etched in stone in the foyer of the administrative building, as well as his photo and bust on display in the Archives in the rear building. Toronto is naming a park after him. The University and Board of Trade appear to have no visible mementos. One wonders whether an institute might have been named after him if his name had been other than Workman. Perhaps one day a television series will be shown about his exploits as an alienist and sleuth. This biography is one small memorial to his memory.

Appendices

THE WORKMAN FAMILY HISTORY IN IRELAND
AND IN THE U.S.A. (1633-1834)

Following the death of the Rev. William Workman in 1633 (see Chapter One), his young family struggled to survive. All felt bitter about his persecution by Archbishop Laud. His sons then took the opportunity to join the Parliamentary Army under Cromwell which was opposed to the Royalists. One son, named William, worked his way up through the ranks to Captain. According to family legends and diaries, he met the charge of Prince Rupert in 1645 at the Battle of Naseby, but there is no official record of this. He certainly joined Cromwell's army in Ireland in 1648-49. Cromwell thanked him for "helping him cut the throats at Drogheda and elsewhere," by rewarding him liberally "with the goods of other people." Captain Workman received, "in compensation of his military service, several tracts of land in the County of Derry, not far from Coleraine, … two town lands in Merlacco" (confiscated from the O'Neals) and two town lands in Armagh. But these material rewards did not bring him wealth or peace, for to take possession he had to fight off the original inhabitants for the local Irish were naturally angry at the confiscation of their lands. Later, during the administration of the catholic Earl of Tyrconnell, the Captain decided to relinquish his legal claims to these lands.[1] To quote Dr. Joseph Workman in his telling of the story: "The land came from the devil and it went back to him."[2]

The Captain moved to County Down, near Donaghadee, east of Belfast. In 1670 he established linen mills in Moneymore, in Antrim, to the east of Ulster's great inland lake, Lough Neagh. He was reputed to be a very handsome and dashing daredevil. One story about him describes an English soldier meeting a woman with a beautiful baby. On hearing her name he exclaimed that he should have guessed. Only a child of Captain Workman could be that handsome.[3] Another story may be related to the same occasion. Samuel Workman (the Captain's younger son) "and his wife were among the spectators at the landing of William of Orange at Carrickfergus on June 14, 1690, and it is remembered, notwithstanding his haste, he stopped and saluted Mrs. Workman; being struck by the beauty of her baby, kissed it."[4]

By the late 1680s the tension between the Irish Catholics and the Protestant settlers had risen to new heights. The Captain had died but his sons joined the exodus of the Protestants to Londonderry. His older son, William, became known as "The Protestant Boy." They were safe only temporarily. In 1689 the walled city was besieged by the army of James II. The city held for a hundred and five days, and was finally relieved by the Protestant forces. The two sons and their wives emerged from the war-scarred walls. They returned to the Moneymore district. "The musket used at the siege by Workman was seen by the writer in 1812," wrote Joseph Workman, Dr. Joseph Workman's father. (This family heirloom had come into the possession of his aunt.)[5] The older son, William, then bought another mill at Brookend. His descendants lived in this area for nearly a hundred years and many of them were buried nearby at Ballenderry.

A touching story about this William's son, Benjamin of Brookend and Moneymore, is recounted by Dr. Benjamin Workman in his diary: "I would rather live in poverty than be always embroiled in quarrels with a bad neighbour," said my great-grandfather, when he resolved to leave his handsome property, consisting of a good mill and farm at Brookend near Coagh, and remove to Moneymore to be the miller of the village mill. And his choice, though attended with a heavy pecuniary loss was a prudent one, for he had peace of mind and lived and died in peace with his neighbours, and in peace with his God. When his wife, an exemplary Presbyterian, died, his Catholic neighbours asked permission to honour her memory by the "Irish cry" at her wake. These kind neighbours gathered round her bier, sprinkled her mortal remains with holy water, formed themselves into a large circle in the chamber of death, and with beads in hand repeated a solemn Rosary for the repose of her soul; and then exhibited their peculiar custom of continuing throughout the whole night the Kenah or Irish cry. Her relatives accepted the civility as a token of respect and good feelings."[6]

This Benjamin had a son named Benjamin, nicknamed "The Honest Miller," who married an Ann Scott who bore him six children. The youngest, named Joseph, was born in 1759, and became the father of the subject of this biography. He and his older brother, Benjamin, trained as teachers. The story goes that there was a famine in the land and one morning 32 beggars were waiting outside Benjamin's schoolhouse. This so depressed him about his future in Ireland that he decided to emigrate to America, the land that everyone was talking about. The American Revolution was over, and immigrants were again arriving en mass. In 1787 Joseph accompanied his older brother to the newly formed States. In his diary he wrote: "Landing at Baltimore on a Sunday we were shocked to view urchins playing ball, having forgotten that Maryland was a Catholic country."[7] They visited their married sister, Ann, in Conecocheaque, Pennsylvania, and then continued on to the capital of their new land, Philadelphia. This bustling and relatively cosmopolitan town was a big change from their small Ulster village. Yet the two young men must have impressed the American colonists, for both secured teaching positions in the college which later became the University of Pennsylvania. Benjamin became a Professor of Mathematics and Geography, while Joseph tutored in Maths and later lectured in English Literature. Benjamin, assisted by his brother, wrote a Geography textbook published in 1790 and used for many years in American schools.[8] They experienced all that Philadelphia had to offer. They became acquainted with the great George Washington, and fell under the spell of Benjamin Franklin, a the venerated scholar, who in his final years had been elected President of the State Council of Pennsylvania. It is of interest that he was a religious free thinker as well as a strong advocate of representative government. Unfortunately, soon after their arrival he became bedridden and died in 1790.[9] Nevertheless, the two brothers were both influenced by his thinking as well as by the ideals of the new American States.

After three years in Philadelphia, Joseph became physically ill and then homesick. He returned to Ireland. First, however, he went to London, England, where he tried to patent a new mariner's compass which his brother had invented. He was tricked by the mechanic who copied the ideas and registered it in his own name, so he gave up the attempt and returned to teaching in the north of Ireland. He left behind four siblings in America, i.e. not only his brother Benjamin (who eventually returned to Ireland), but also a sister and two other brothers. The descendants of his sister, Ann Collins (later Logan), moved west from Pennsylvania to Lisbon on the banks of the Ohio. His brother John settled at first near his sister, then in Virginia, where he became disgusted at living in a "slave state," so he eventually moved west to Sangammon County, Illinois, where he established his own post office. The second brother, Samuel, was a sea captain. His family settled in New Orleans. A son of Samuel became a judge who was drowned in Lake Pontchartain in 1834.

Thus the Irish branch of the family maintained strong American connections.[10] When Joseph's family later emigrated to Canada, they remained very sympathetic to the U.S.A. They also favoured free trade between Canada and the States. When the Workmans were living in Montreal, the Unitarian Congregation of New Orleans invited the Unitarian minister of Montreal (the Rev. John Cordner from the north of Ireland) to preach and minister there for a few months. Perhaps this was related to the Workman connection.

APPENDIX TWO

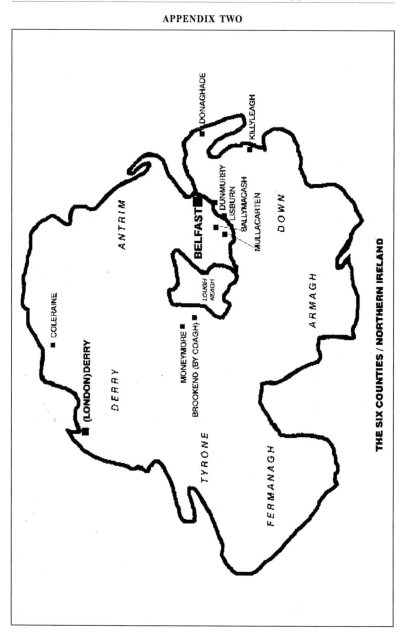

APPENDIX THREE

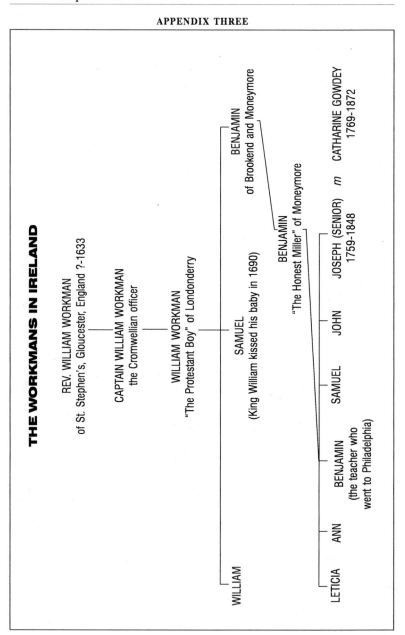

THE WORKMANS IN IRELAND

REV. WILLIAM WORKMAN
of St. Stephen's, Gloucester, England ?-1633

CAPTAIN WILLIAM WORKMAN
the Cromwellian officer

WILLIAM WORKMAN
"The Protestant Boy" of Londonderry

SAMUEL
(King William kissed his baby in 1690)

BENJAMIN
of Brookend and Moneymore

BENJAMIN
"The Honest Miller" of Moneymore

WILLIAM

LETICIA   ANN   BENJAMIN   SAMUEL   JOHN   JOSEPH (SENIOR)   m   CATHARINE GOWDEY
                  (the teacher who   1759-1848   1769-1872
                  went to Philadelphia)

APPENDIX FOUR

WORKMAN FAMILY IN CANADA
(descended from Dr. Joseph and Elizabeth Wasnidge)

JOSEPH WORKMAN SR. & CATHARINE GOWDEY
1759-1848   1769-1872

Children:

DR. BENJAMIN 1794-1878
ALEXANDER 1798-1891
JOHN 1803-1829
DR. JOSEPH 1805-1894
WILLIAM 1807-1878
ANN 1809-1882
SAMUEL 1811-1869
THOMAS 1813-1889
MATTHEW FRANCIS 1815-1839

WILLIAM 1836-1895
m
Jane Clarke

FRED 1838-1887

MATTHEW 1840-1840 (died at 5 mths)

JOSEPH 1841-1904

BENJAMIN 1843-1844 (died at 13 mths)

ANNA 1847-1922
m
Dr. John E. Kennedy

CATHARINE 1848-1849 (died at 17 mths)

THOMAS 1850-1938

FLORENCE (Florie) 1852-1910

ALFRED 1857-1858 (died at 10 mths)

ELIZABETH (Bessie) 1877-1969
m
William Baker

CHARLES

JOSEPH

WILLIAM

HAROLD

CATHARINE
m
Charles Haynes

WILLIAM BAKER 1904-1979

JOHN (Jack) BAKER of Montreal 1907-

MARY (Madie) BAKER
m
GRAVES 1910-1995

JOHN (Jack) C. HAYNES

ANNE BAKER 1933-1996
m
Glen Hadley

WILLIAM BAKER 1935-1981

THOMAS BAKER 1939-

JOHN HAYNES

KEITH HADLEY

SUSAN HADLEY

PETER HADLEY

Postscript:
DR. BEN WORKMAN's descendants in Uxbridge area
ANNE WORKMAN m. DR. JOSEPH BASCOM (of Uxbridge)
(adopted a girl who married NEWTON ST. JOHN)

BASCOM ST. JOHN   JUDITH ST. JOHN   ELIZABETH ST. JOHN

B E N ' S   S T O R Y
(as told in his diary)
A. IRELAND (1794-1819)

Benjamin Workman, Joseph's oldest brother, was born on November 4, 1794. Dr. Joseph Workman was eleven years younger and was much influenced by his oldest brother. In his formative years Benjamin became his first schoolteacher. Later on in Toronto, it was Benjamin whom Joseph invited to assist him for nineteen years in his important work at the Asylum. Benjamin kept a detailed diary of these early years in Ballymacash, and so more is known about his childhood than about any of the others. Some of his descriptions give a flavour of growing up in Northern Ireland at the turn of the century, and the environment in which Workman children were raised.

Until Ben was three and a half, he was the only child and received a great deal of attention. His father forbade him playing with the local boys because of their bad language and behaviour, which suggests a certain snobbishness in Joseph Workman, Senior. Ben spent much time alone, or with adults, such as his parents or the local workmen (whose language, according to Ben, was much worse than the local children's). Then the siblings began to arrive, but they were all considerably younger, and not, at first, good playmates. Ben was a very scholarly boy who desired above all else to attend school. Money was short and the Ballymacash school, which would have been free for Ben, had been temporarily closed when his father, the teacher, became the estate factor. The father disapproved of reading novels, so Ben started his serious reading with the Bible, which he thoroughly enjoyed. He went on to other ambitious works such as Pope's *Essay on Man*, which he read at aged ten, and henceforth (according to Ben), lost his taste for juvenile literature. He next borrowed from his Aunt Sarah Gowdey's husband, a copy of Guthrie's *Gazeteer and Geography*. His father meanwhile was teaching him Arithmetic and

Business, hoping that Ben might start up his own business one day. Ben worked his way quickly through Gough's *Arithmetic*, enjoying the logic and the magic of numbers. His father wanted him to be apprenticed in the muslin and linen trade which was one of the key industries in Ireland at that time. Benjamin complied reluctantly, but it appears to have been a subtle battle between two stubborn people. Ben insisted that he tried hard but he worked very slowly and once got all the threads so entangled that the owner had to throw out the weave. The owner then charged Ben's father for the thread! The father finally gave in. He had so much respect for learning that it was hard for him to deny Ben schooling. But three years later he persuaded Ben to try again and this time he was more successful. The financial rewards for Ben were, however, meagre. His father took his earnings and he was given 1/2 penny each Sunday which had to be put in the poor box and not spent on frivolities. Thus did the Workman parents instill "Christian responsibility" and charitable giving in their children.

By 1810 the linen industry was beginning to run into hard times, with poor future prospects, so Ben and his father reassessed the situation. Despite working for several years, Ben was not far behind in his education because he had taken advantage of every opportunity for schooling, often completing three years work in one. He was very poor in penmanship, however, according to his own account. So he persuaded his father to let him return to school in order to improve his writing, which was a necessary aspect of business in those days. He attended Mr. Shields' School in nearby Lisburn, and won the first premium in Grammar. There is no record whether his writing improved or not! Next he went to the Lisburn Academy and studied Classics. He finally got a teaching job nearby at Mullacarten, working on his High School exams in the evening. (This beautiful red sandstone building is still standing, converted into a private home, and a photo of it is included in the illustrations.)

On completion of his High school certificate, Ben became a teaching assistant at what is now known as the Royal Belfast Academical Institute, a prestigious private school, which was then called the Academical Section of Belfast College. The wife of the headmaster of the English Department had wanted to hire only teachers from England, so she was upset by Ben's presence on staff. One day, without any provocation from him, she called him one of "the savage Irish," and threatened to "have him horsewhipped." He verbally stood up to her and thus ended his sojourn at the Institute.[1] Ben handled this traumatic event relatively well for he did not dwell long on this misfortune. In 1817 he returned to teaching at Mullacarten. But in 1819 Benjamin reported that he could no longer stand the poverty and the begging around him, an echo of his uncle's and father's words back in 1787. Ireland had once again been hit by poor harvests, and fields of rotting potatoes. Typhus was rampant. So Ben emigrated to Canada, all by himself, wearing a new suit and with only twenty five guineas in his pocket.

B. CANADA (1819-1878)

Benjamin had no desire to be a farmer but he had thought of settling in Upper Canada, so in the summer of 1820 he travelled up the St Lawrence river to Prescott. In 1815 the Lachine Canal had been opened, connecting Montreal and the ocean with the inland navigation system. Ben found the trip an exciting experience. The United Empire Loyalists from the States fascinated him and impressed him with their thrift, energy, and large but plain farms. The Yankee etiquette of Ogdensburg astounded him with its frankness. But best of all he enjoyed dinner at the famous Crysler's Farm, where Mrs. Crysler entertained him, and afterwards he wrote:

"I inquired how she felt when the enemy (the invading American army) made his appearance. She replied in a very spirited and sprightly manner 'Oh I knew they were coming long before they came in sight, and felt kind of queer thinking they might take it into their head to burn the House but they didn't, they only took my cows and sheep and killed them for meat. When I saw this work going on I went to the

General (Wilkinson) and asked him who was going to pay me for them. He gave me bits of paper for them and said 'You shall have your pay as soon as we get to Montreal.' I looked at him and laughed and asked him 'Do you ever think you'll get to Montreal? No, not a bit of it, General! You'll never get there; our boys are coming and they'll soon settle that with you. You'll never set a foot in Montreal.' "[2] Benjamin wrote immediately to his family back in Ireland, and recounted this story. He knew his father would be interested in the stories about the battle of Crysler's Farm in which the British-Canadian army defeated the Americans in 1813, effectively driving them out of Canada.

Ben was lonely in Montreal, but he was very careful in seeking out new friends, choosing to associate only with those who held sympathetic religious views. Finding no "new light" Presbyterian or Unitarian church to attend, he decided to attend a traditional Presbyterian church and not to "abandon public worship because I could not concur in every item of the Church's creed. Previous to the first Sacramental occasion I waited on the minister, told him that I did not believe in the Trinity, Vicarious Atonement or Predestination. His reply was that the Communion Table was not his but the Lord's, and that he bade everyone welcome there who acknowledged the same God and was willing faithfully to serve Him. I gratefully availed myself of the permission thus liberally accorded."[3]

The Unitarians of that time were not numerous enough to start their own congregation. They were recorded as attending both St. Andrew's Presbyterian and St. Gabriel Street Church. Later on, the American Presbyterian Church was founded and Unitarians also attended there. Although an attempt was made in 1832 to start their own congregation, it was not until 1842 that the Christian Unitarian Society of Montreal was permanently established, in which Ben played a key role.[4]

Ben's first marriage and the establishment of the Union school is described in Chapter 3. After the death of his first wife in 1829, Ben decided to leave the school in charge of Alexander, assisted at that time by Joseph, while he began another career as a journalist. Together with another Unitarian, Ariel Bowman, he bought the *Canadian Courant* newspaper. They discreetly promoted liberal views in religion, social welfare issues, and the temperance movement, a cause dear to his heart and characteristic of the reform movement of that time. Indeed he blamed the distilleries for helping to close the paper down in 1834.[5] He then began his third career, that of a pharmacist. During this time he remarried, an American named Mary Anne Mills.

Misfortunes continued to follow Ben. His only son, Joseph Philo, died on September 30, 1842, aged 10 months, followed a year later by his second wife. His two daughters, Mary Matilda and Anne Mills Workman, were then raised by their energetic grandmother, Catharine Workman. (Ben later lived with Anne, after she married Dr. Joseph Bascom of Uxbridge, Ontario.)[6] These losses seemed to compound Ben's tendency to quarrelsomeness. The proud perseverance and kindness evident in his younger days became more of an arrogant self-righteousness in his middle years. One of his redeeming features, however, was his charitable work in the early 1850s. As a pharmacist and newly trained doctor (graduating in 1853) he offered his services free to many poor people. He sponsored several orphans as well as a "repentant" prostitute, who had become an unwed mother. It is a touching story. If she had accepted the help of the Magdalen Sisters, she would have had to give up her baby to a "foundling home." A horrified Ben offered to support mother and baby. Unfortunately the baby did not survive long.[7]

In 1855 Ben unfortunately entered into a major fight with his minister, the Rev. John Cordner. This resulted in his resignation from the Management Committee of the Christian Unitarian Society of Montreal. Since the church had become his second home, this created a serious loss of face for him. He has been called the Patriarch of the congregation, because of his contributions to its founding. The first service had been held in his Union School in 1832 because none of the Montreal churches would rent them their premises. He had assisted two women in resurrecting the congregation after the first attempt died. He had arranged with the Rev. Henry Montgomery and the Remonstrant Synod of Ireland to send out a newly ordained minister to Montreal, as part of their missionary outreach. (The American Unitarians had not managed to supply a permanent minister.) But his young and gifted protégé, the Rev. John Cordner, had a mind of his own, and refused to relinquish some of the ministerial power to the Board of Elders, as Ben had requested. The congregation finally supported the minister against Ben, and Ben felt devastated.[8] This final vote took place in 1856, and influenced him to accept Joseph's invitation to leave Montreal.

As mentioned earlier, Joseph maintained a close relationship with his eldest brother during the twenty years since leaving Montreal. He had influenced Ben to enter medicine in 1850. He trusted and admired Ben, and he invited him to assist him at the Asylum in 1856. Ben also admired Joseph and was humble enough to accept direction from his younger brother when the time came. He was able to work under Joseph for nineteen years.

When the lonely Ben came to Toronto he found a real home in the Unitarian Congregation there. He seemed to outgrow his quarrelsomeness, for the Toronto records are full of his kindly and devoted leadership. He became highly respected again.[9] He had a rare ability to mix easily with the wealthy and the poorer members, a characteristic also observed in Montreal, and this made him an invaluable leader and communicator.[10] After moving to Toronto he frequently visited Montreal, the city of his many triumphs and defeats. Even his funeral service in 1878 was held in Montreal. The procession left from Thomas's house; the service was held in the Unitarian Church of the Messiah (the new name); and he was buried in the Mount Royal cemetery.[11] In death all was forgiven.

JOSEPH'S CORRESPONDENCE WITH CHURCH LEADERS
(1853-1855)
Letters from Joseph to the Minister or the Board of Trustees of the First Congregation of Toronto concerning the conflict around whether to hold a mortgage or not on the church property

BACKGROUND HISTORY:

Joseph, under the auspices of the Workman Brothers Hardware business, lent the congregation most of the money to buy their first building, the George Street chapel. This was repaid fairly quickly. He served on the Board for 6 years as secretary and then for another two and a half as the chair of the Building Committee. The Rev. Charles Dall arrived in 1850. (This minister was later to become famous in NW India where he worked successfully for 30 years.) Relationships between Joseph and the minister seemed very cordial until late 1853. Indeed, when the minister went on vacation, Joseph was invited to lead the first service in his absence.

In 1853 the Board sent the minister to the U.S.A. on a lengthy fund-raising tour to collect donations for a brand new building, and while on tour, he also took extensive sick leave. During his absence, estimated costs for the project escalated, and on August 3, five members of the Board, including Joseph, generously offered to lend 100 pounds each. On November 8, Joseph resigned from the Board, probably because of his new position at the Asylum, but he remained on the Building Fund Committee. He then offered to lend 5 shares worth 500 pounds instead of the cash loan mentioned above, if the congregation took out a mortgage as security and paid him the interest involved. Another member said he could borrow the money more cheaply through friends. Joseph congratulated him and seemed very pleased with the alternative arrangement. Joseph did not say why he had withdrawn the original offer of 100 pounds. Perhaps he foresaw costs escalating further (which they did) and a long delay in the return of the loan. Since he had only a temporary post at the Asylum, his own future career (and income) was insecure.

When the Rev. Charles Dall returned, he eventually discovered the change in plans. On November 21 and 22, 1853, he wrote two letters to Joseph begging him to return to the original offer of August. He said he had promised the donors on his fund-raising tour that there would be no mortgage and that five members had generously offered loans to avoid the shame of a mortgage. The other four members had agreed to change back to the original plan. The concern was that a small congregation would be laden with heavy expenses. This concern was very valid but there was conflict over solutions. The following questions were raised. Must promises be kept at all costs? Should a few members be asked to sacrifice for the group? Should the minister be involved in financial decisions, bearing in mind, of-course, that recently he had been sent on a major fund-raising trip, and was thus automatically involved?

The first letter printed here was Joseph's personal reply to the Rev. Charles Dall. The minister then shared it with the Board and congregation. It reads as a rather mean-spirited letter and was shared without Joseph's permission, so he was extremely upset. This letter, dated November 26, 1853, reads as follows:

Dear Sir,
I have read notes of 21 and 22 and have given careful consideration to the contents. Apprehending that you are placing yourself in a wrong position in your interference with the management of the secular affairs of the church, especially when you urge the reversal of a formal act of the Trustees before that body have reconsidered the subject at issue, I respectfully decline all present discussion. If I have afforded to me the opportunity of explaining my own position and purpose to my brethren in a congregational meeting, I trust to be able to satisfy them of my integrity as well as my unchanged zeal in the great cause of Chris-

tian truth. In the meantime I cannot fail to perceive, from the tenor of your communications, that you have been misinformed as to the actual position of the affairs of the Society, or that you have strangely misapprehended the facts communicated to you. The peace and safety of the church, I believe to be much imperilled by the untoward tendency of your proceedings, and as a faithful member I desire to have an early adjustment of all difficulties; but in the management of the temporal concerns of our Society I shall, as ever heretofore I have done, urge the propriety of exempting the pastor from all connection therewith.

I remain, Dear and Rev. Sir,

Yours in the Faith,

Joseph Workman

At the Congregational Meeting of December 8, it was moved and then seconded by Joseph to expunge the minister's letters and the replies, from the Minutes of the Board of Trustees. It was followed by a motion expressing confidence in the minister's piety and devotedness. A third motion was to establish a Constitutional Review Committee of five members which included Joseph.

Next came a generous letter of apology from the minister to Joseph. Here is Joseph's reply:

Dear Sir,

Yours of 17th reached me by post and should have had earlier attention had my time permitted. The difficulty which has recently arisen between you & me, having been regarded by me as a public and not personal concern, I have nothing to forgive. If you had viewed the matter in a different light, I regret the misunderstanding. Any explanation to you of my opinions and feelings upon the subject beyond that which I have already given in my proper place as a member of the congregation, I consider not only uncalled for but quite inexpedient. If the peace of the church is to be preserved, it is indispensable that both pastor & member take care not to permit matters of public reference to be transformed into causes of personal and unchristian animosity. I beg to assure you that towards yourself & family I have ever had but one feeling, that of kindness, and the desire of advancing your welfare & happiness, concurrently with those of our common church. This is not the proper occasion for expatiating on the injury to my feelings & social propriety sustained in the course of the recent discussion on the pecuniary affairs of our Society. I am not a Unitarian of yesterday and be assured it will require harder knocks than I have yet felt to drive me from the ranks of the workers and the faithful.

Please accept 5/- enclosed for your school,* and may God speed you.

With most heartfelt wishes for your happiness & that of your family, I remain, in the brotherhood of the faith, most firmly yours,

J. Workman

---

*The Rev. Dall had begun an evening school for working boys and young men, and had asked for contributions to pay for expenses.

In May 1854, the Board of Trustees talked of instituting a suit to compel Joseph to transfer the lot to the ownership of the congregation, but were advised that there were legal difficulties delaying the transfer, not any resistance on Joseph's part. The conclusion was that the lot would have to be registered in the name of the Board of Trustees, not that of the congregation. Soon after the minister resigned because of another breakdown in his health. One Trustee resigned because of the "ungrateful conduct of a portion of this congregation to their pastor," but he did remain a church member.

On June 5 Joseph was reelected to the Board but resigned June 19 in order to aid the transfer of the lot from his name to that of the

Board of Trustees. He wrote:

> I have received your note of today informing me of an intended meeting of the Trustees of the Toronto Unitarian Congregation, on Thursday evening next, and inquiring of behalf of the Board whether I am prepared to make the loan of 100 pounds as promised by me last summer in aid of the building fund, or whether I am still willing to loan to the congregation the proceeds of five shares in the Home District Building Society, as subsequently proposed by me. Anticipating that I may not find myself able to attend the proposed meeting of the board, and feeling besides no trivial reluctance to be again mixed up with the proceedings of a Society in which I have been treated with very unmerited indignity, I forward to you for information of the Board a written reply.
>
> I have never receded from any engagement entered into by me with the church, and do not desire to do so. Before however renewing negotiations on either proposition I wish to be favoured with a full statement of the present fiscal condition of the church, showing the sums collected for building purposes, and the amount distributed for the same, together with all obligations outstanding on the contracts, or formally borrowed by the Trustees to meet current requirements, also the amount with details of uncollected subscriptions.
>
> Permit me to add that being anxious to complete the con— (?) of the church lot to the Society, I deem it most expedient to decline acting as a Trustee and hereby tender through you my resignation of the office with the hope that you will appoint a permanent successor.
>
> Yours, Joseph Workman, M.D.

The response to this letter must have been very supportive because the tone of Joseph's next letter, dated July 5, 1854, is very positive:

Dear Sir,

I have your favour of yesterday informing me that the Trustees of our Church have accepted my offer of the proceeds of Home District Building Society Stock. In reply I beg to state that I shall be ready to execute the necessary documents at any moment you may apprize me of their being ready for my signature. I enclose hereby the application for the loan from the B.S. . . .

As to future subscriptions for Church operations, you may put my name down for 15 pounds a year, to the fund for minister's salary should the church engage one. You will please in my name assure the Trustees and members of my cordial cooperation and pecuniary aid, in all their operations and necessities. The church has ever been among the objects dearest to my heart; and as long as God spares me life and health I trust never to forsake it, in whatsoever trial. Let us forget the past; and learn from our experience prudent forethought, no more weaving (?) circles.

Yours truly,

Joseph Workman, M.D.

On August 9 the Board voted to accept Joseph's offer of the loan of his shares and to take out a mortgage from the same company. He replied on August 12:

Gentlemen,

I beg hereby to intimate to you that I am about to transfer to the Directors of the Home District Building Society the Mortgage made by you to me bearing date Ist Instant, on a certain lot of ground on Jarvis Street & the Church erected thereon by the Unitarian Congregation of this city, of which you are the present Trustees.

Yours respectfully,

Joseph Workman, M.D.

On January 16, 1855, Joseph was again reelected to the Board of Trustees. He was too busy at the Asylum to be very involved. He resigned (for the third time) on September 3, 1855. On November 14, 1855, he offered to buy the part of the lot bordering on Mutual Street, which the Board had placed for sale in July to help diminish the debt on the new building.

Thus Joseph ended ten years of very intensive involvement with the Unitarian Congregation. He remained a member, and contributed financially on and off till his death.

APPENDIX SEVEN

LETTERS WRITTEN BY ELIZABETH WORKMAN
TO HER SON WILLIAM
(1854-1864)

July 25, 1854

. . . Mr. Dall is in Boston. Mrs. Dall is living here just now. Mr. Patton has had the cholera. I drove past the church the other day. It looks better than I expected. I feel very sorry for Mr. Dall. It is to bad to have to leave when the church is nearly finished. Mrs. Dall will never ____? for any but for her own country ladies and ours foolish enough to feel hurt because she thinks they are not worth talking to. She did not know how to play her cards on this side or else she would have gained the Ladies and then she might have kept the Gentlemen.

Mr. Hincks preaches frequently but Mr. Hosmer_? has recommended them to write to Meadville for a Scotchman whom he thinks will suit our congregation so he has been invited to come for a time. Willie Burgess had a touch of cholera. He is now in the country. Pa has not been in the city for weeks. I hope you wear flannel and above all things don't take it off at night. Woolen socks Pa says are absolutely necessary.

Old Mr. Latham wishes to be remembered to Uncle Benjamin. He is confined to bed this long time. I think he will not live over the summer. He complains none of the Congregation go to see him except Mr. Hincks. Mr. Hamilton is going to live at the Hen and Chickens near Owen Sound. He is going into partnership with Mr. Master in some mills he has likewise built, a saw mill of his own, about 20 miles from Penetanguishine so I think he is in fair way for getting rich.

March 8, 1859

… Mrs. Eastwood's baby is a fine healthy child, very fat. I think the father spends half his time nursing it. She has made up her mind to stay where she is and not go to Ireland this year, the idea of him giving up his situation for some insane whim of hers. Pa says she is so foolish that he cannot endure the sight of her. She leads her husband by the nose and makes him believe everything. Even Uncle Ben has no influence over Mr. Eastwood.

Mr. Eastwood's brother, the doctor, is here on a visit. He has been several years on the coast of Africa and Mrs. E. intends that he should take her with him as far as Ireland next month. Old Mr. E. told me she was sure he would not and so I think that is the reason for the change of mind. If you were just to the account of the niggers at home he says they are a hundred times better off in slavery. He says they are an awful people. He is religious but he says the talk of missionary is all humbug about those people anyway. He says you could not confer a quicker blessing on them than to bring them here and make slaves of them. You can never do them any good at home. They are so utterly devoid of every social feeling.

N.B. John Scott has been sick – consumption; and Pa insisted on going to Fort Malden altho he did not seem well because of the urgency of overcrowding and his pressing of the government for space. Governor ordered him to go.

Undated Letter of 1864:

    … Pa has been very busy making out the estimates, writing reports, etc. etc. – nearly fagged out.

DR. WORKMAN'S COMMENTS ON SUNDAY VISITORS
(1860)

I saw them sitting on the grass – a mother, father and three children. They had spread a blanket and sat sunning themselves. The mother wore a wide-brimmed white hat with a flowered band that hung from it in the back. The father was in his straw. A boy wore a sailor suit like the royal prince. They opened a hamper and mother passed out sandwiches. Father pointed out one Mary K. to the children. Mary's hair was dishevelled and she walked with the peculiar gate of those long confined to the ward. It was a shuffle, with stomach out and shoulders back, the arms limp at the sides. Her vacant looks and dribbling mouth frightened the girls, but made the little boy laugh. When she lifted her dress and watered a bed of flowers, the father roared out and the mother was scandalized.

    They had come here for entertainment. They had made a picnic of it. To them these unfortunates were freaks in some country fair side show – to be gawked at, shuddered at, laughed at and forgotten. At no time did the parents wonder if Mary had ever been a little girl like their daughters or if she had a husband or a son. She was sub-human. She was a human. Dehumanized.

    Then they left, to go to church.

GLOBE ARTICLE ON JOSEPH'S ANNUAL REPORT (1874)

The battle between Joseph and the Globe *continued for decades, as exemplified by this* Globe *article on Joseph's annual report, dated Dedember 12, 1874, and entitled "Official Reports."*

*   *   *

Solomon has left on record his conviction that there is a time for everything, and the very best things when inappropriate become offensive. A perusal of the seventh annual report of the Inspector of Asylums and Prisons, etc., for the Province of Ontario makes us keenly alive to the truth of the wise king's remark. Two or three of the reports sent to Mr. Langmuir are disfigured by painful attempts at smartness, and ghastly attempts at humour. A report is expected to be direct, business-like, concise; and if a man with the wit of Rabelais had to write the account of a year's management of a prison or asylum the display of it would be an impertinence. The greatest offender in this respect is Dr. Joseph Workman, the medical superintendent of the Asylum for the Insane, Toronto. We shall content ourselves with a few instances. At page 154 we read:- "The recovery of the two longest resident females, who were both very well known to you, did not take place recently. Both might have been discharged long ago, had any comfortable home been commandable. One was nearly seventy years of age, and had for years suffered intense mental agony, under the malevolence of an evil spirit, which used very bad language and kept her in terrible bondage. Happily this persecutor at last gave up his naughty tricks, and we had the unspeakable happiness of seeing our good honest friend go back home to her kindred, sound in mind and very fat in body." Possibly the doctor thinks this a pretty piece of writing, and at the same time full of delicate humour. But in an official document it would be better to curb his fancy, and content himself with a plain statement. Again on page 160, "In last year's Public Accounts, I, by chance, saw (for I was not honoured with a copy nor with one of the Annual Estimates) that the year's expenditure was augmented by adding thereto the receipts from the paying patients and articles sold, thus making our drawings on the Provincial Exchequer figure up some forty thousand dollars more than the real amount. Not being an accredited accountant, I am unable to say whether this system of book-keeping is correct or otherwise; but it looks very much like that of my countryman who balanced a calf on his lean horse's back, by slinging a stone on the other side to keep things square. The horse, of course, was not consulted. Asses cannot lower their dignity by deferring to the opinion of horses, yet it seems to me a strange way of putting facts, and certainly not very encouraging toward the cultivation of Asylum revenue.

The liberal publishers of Canada merit the continued gratitude of our people. I wish I could include the *Globe* and *Mail* in the list, but these journals have lunatics enough outside this Asylum to find food for, without adding to their number."

We have heard before of lunatics who thought all the outside world mad, but never before did we see the idea developed in an official report. The Superintendent too, evidently labours under the delusion that there is some reason for the proprietor of a paper supplying copies gratis to an asylum which does not apply equally to a butcher supplying meat. In writing a report, attempts to show cleverness are evidences of an unbalanced, uncultivated mind.

APPENDIX TEN
ADDRESS GIVEN BY DR. JOSEPH WORKMAN TO TORONTO MEDICAL STUDENTS (1883)
Published in the *Matrix,* July, 1980
(Staff publication of Queen Street Mental Health Centre)
with the following introduction:

In response to many requests we are reproducing the text of an address delivered by Dr. Joseph Workman to a group of medical students. The address was re-created by noted actor Dan MacDonald at Queen Street Mental Health Centre as part of our 130th anniversary celebrations.

*   *   *

I've been asked to bore you for a few minutes as part of the penance you must pay for becoming clinicians in Ontario.

Though now surrounded by houses on all sides, this structure was, when erected, wholly in the country. It was in 1846 that the original building was commenced, the corner stone being laid by Chief Justice Robinson with becoming ceremonial, on Saturday, August 22nd, of that year.

The old homestead of the Shaw family, a little to the north-east was then the residence of Captain Alexander Shaw. He farmed some 50 acres to the north of where I stand today. The Givins' house was a little to the west. There were few homes on Queen Street, and of course, my staff knew of the Blue Bell tavern, afterwards destroyed by fire, and, if memory serves, there was another tavern on the eastern corner of Queen and Dundas streets. Mr. Fennings Taylor's residence was to the west. The whole of the rest of the land was either uncleared or cultivated as farms or gardens. Trinity College was not even thought of and there was no school, church or chapel within several miles north or east, and only a small place of worship – Methodist – about a mile west.

When the hospital opened, males were on the west side and females on the east. In the basement there were larders and dairies, and all the necessary offices and dormitories for 20 male and 20 female patients. On the first floor, dormitories for another 36 patients, dining rooms and parlours for convalescent patients. Then there was the matron's chamber and private rooms for house steward and the assistant physician. My brother Benjamin, had served in that post.

In the upper story there were three chapels, an anatomical room and a museum. There was also a room for working patients. The dome was covered with bright tin and it was possible, on a sunshiny day, to see the glittering tower from 20 miles distant.

When I had been in Quebec, a wooden building, originally erected as a Cholera Hospital in 1832, was converted in 1835 into a temporary asylum. That cholera epidemic had killed a full third of all Montrealers. There was nothing elsewhere in Canada for the insane. Nothing in this part of the continent. So when the asylum was built as Canada's largest Government building it surely was a unique undertaking.

I recall an article in the *Globe* newspaper, during my term as superintendent here, it said that there were three asylums within three miles of each other. Queen Street was the largest. From it people sometimes emerged with a whole mind. From the other two, no one ever emerged sound in mind – they were the Legislature and City Hall. Sir John A. MacDonald, the man who dragged us all, kicking and screaming, into this confederation, about which I had my grave doubts, Sir John A. said he encouraged building the hospital as a place to house Grits, so they need not roam the countryside unattended. Well we were country then. Toronto had about 20,000 inhabitants and Queen Street only went up to 282. Once they moved to the 900 block the city Fathers petitioned that we be moved – to Hamilton.

A patient of mine was asked by a *Gazette* reporter how he liked politicians coming in and poking about. They did that before I came and said the smell here was due to the patients. It turned out they forgot to lay sewer tile from the kitchen and the food wastes had formed a five foot swamp under the floor. And, if the ladies will forgive me for being indelicate, they forgot to ventilate the privies. Anyway, they asked old John about these politicians and he said: "You can always spot one of them. They've got liquor on their breath and manure on their shoes." Farm types. Well, the typesetter must have had a drink or two himself, because the article twisted old John so that they had the smell of liquor on their shoes, and on their breath … politeness forbids me to explore this further.

At one time there was (sic) 127 acres here and behind us, instead of a factory belching Lord knows what poison, there was (sic) the Provincial Exhibition Grounds. But things changed.

There were men then, there are in every age, who every time they spoke the sum total of human knowledge was greatly diminished. These men tried to run this hospital on a pittance. I railed against them. Fought them. For 22 years. Finally, I retired, not because I was old. Seventy was not old. But because of those who knew the least, saying the most. And having the power to be listened to by those who should know better.

Toronto the good. City of churches, 22 to be exact, its citizens would pack a picnic lunch and come to gaze on the misfortunes of others and be amused. They'd laugh and point at the sick and chortle at bizarre behaviour. Enlightened, civilized, Christian Toronto. There was sickness, all right. You young people are sailing uncharted waters. You'll navigate new courses in unfamiliar streams, meet many dead ends, become grounded on sandbars of public ignorance, becalmed by lack of funds for your research and suffer many a gale. The less hardy will abandon ship. The brave may yet reach the distant shore where sits understanding of these sicknesses, waiting to greet the fearless sailors of the deep, troubled waters of madness.

It is too easy to forget that the ends we serve is not our careers – to rise in our profession and receive accolades from our peers – but humanity. If we are no better than pedlars seeking profit, albeit in honours not dollars, then we should leave medicine. I'll return to my one-time role of hardware merchant, at which I was very successful, and you to whatever clerk's roles you wish. The easiest thing to do is lock the insane in cells and feed them and forget them. The hardest is to find that spark of humanity that dwells in each of us. We all are tempted to quit the race at one time or another. But, as was said so very long ago, the race is not to the swift. No, it is to he who perseveres. I pass the torch to you. Carry it proudly to Olympus itself. God speed and goodbye.

APPENDIX ELEVEN

MATRIX COMMENTS ON NAMING
THE DR. JOSEPH WORKMAN AUDITORIUM
(July 1980)

DR. WORKMAN VISITS QUEEN STREET;

HISTORIC ADDRESS RECREATED

Over 200 staff and members of the general public came to the cafeteria on January 25, for refreshments and an address by Dr. Joseph Workman, recreated by actor Dan MacDonald (past President of Equity). Staff had an opportunity to wear their T-shirts and buttons in honour of the 130th anniversary; some came in period dress to make the doctor feel at home.

Workman spoke of the needs of the patients, the needs for research, and the importance of community acceptance of the mentally ill. The address, originally given to graduating medical students in 1883 when Workman was 78 years old, was surprisingly relevant some 100 years later. The doctor described the Queen and Ossington area long before streets and houses were there; and he also spoke of the early years of medicine in Ontario. Those from the community who came to hear the speech were moved by the eloquence of both language and delivery.

Matrix photo caption:

Dan MacDonald as Dr. Workman sits with Queen Street Mental Health Centre staff in period costume. Back row: Angela Brehm, Ken

Reed, Winston Stapleford, Richard Mickiewicz, Chris McManus. Centee row: Raphael De Veyra, Jean Mead, Mary Young, Vivienne Gibbs, Dan MacDonald, Maggie Lee.

APPENDIX TWELVE
87TH BIRTHDAY LETTERS
(1892)

"Rockwood," Kingston
26 May, 1892

Dear Dr. Workman –

It is a great pleasure to all of us at Rockwood to be able to congratulate you today. Personally I have always felt that one of the brightest spots in my life has been my friendship with you, and I thoroughly appreciate the advantage that it has been to have had the benefit of your advice and direction. It must be a satisfaction to you to know that all young men who have fallen under your inspiration have been encouraged in a manner that has made their lives purer and better – Yours has been an ideal life and those of us who love you best would express the admiration we feel –

If the thousands of unfortunate insane who experienced the gentle rule under which you cared for them and restored many of them to reason, could speak and add their contributions to this volume of congratulations you would realize that you have not lived in vain, but have achieved the highest ideal that a man can strive for, viz – that of having existed not for the glorification of himself, but for the happiness of others. There are few of us perhaps who fully understand what your influence on asylum management has been in Ontario – your labours have not been appreciated to the extent that they should have been by the general public. But after all is not the undying gratitude of a suffering humanity far more grateful than the loud sounding applause of a thoughtless multitude –

I know that in my work the precepts and examples laid down by you, come home to me with peculiar force almost every hour and when I allow them to act as guiding stars I never go astray – Many years have passed since a merry band of "Clinicals" met you day by day in the Board Room – a cruel fate has claimed one of the number for its own, and all of us have reached a time when shadows are beginning to grow more in command than of yore but those of us who live are as a unit in our regard for the good old man who has been a father to them – Let me then my dear friend wish you many happy returns of the day – and it is my earnest prayer that you may be spared many years.

Believe me

Yours affectionately

C. K. Clarke

*   *   *

Elora, 26 May, 1892

My Dear Friend,

The return of your birthday reminds me that we are both growing old. 1826 witnessed my birth and your majority and yet somehow or other the sixty-six years which have intervened have scarcely taught me to realize your age or my own. It seems as if but a score of them had passed since I formed that acquaintance with you which so speedily ripened into friendship, and it is difficult to call up the conviction that for more than forty years I have known you so intimately.

But however hard it may be to feel the quick passage of time, it is easy to remember the influence, which from its inception, my intercourse with you had upon my lines of thought, my opinions and my actions. I was but a young man when I first knew you, with but little knowledge of the world, although burning with desire to know more, with imperfect ideas of men and their doings, but possessed of a determination to reform both; with crude notions of politics and politicians, and yet thoroughly convinced that they could be purified and exalted by the inky outpourings of a callow sub-editor. I had much to learn and you generously became my mentor.

Your kindly criticism, your valued suggestions, your timely hints, your rich fund of varied knowledge, your intimate acquaintance with Canada and Canadians, your experience, so much greater than mine, were freely placed at my disposal and, while profiting far less from your sound advice than was within the possibilities, I can never forget how willingly it was given and how thankfully appreciated.

Of other ties that have sprung up between us it is unnecessary to speak. They have been productive of much happiness and intense satisfaction and of deep consolation, too, at times of trial, to both of us, and neither of us, I am sure, regrets that they were formed. Remembering all this, I heartily join with those who, on this anniversary, tender their congratulations to you and are unanimous in the hope that you may be spared yet longer to witness the bright sunset of a century of which you saw the grey and threatening morning, but which has done so much to make the world a better dwelling-place for intelligent men and women.

I am, My dear friend,
Ever faithfully yours
Charles Clarke

*   *   *

Aylum for the Insane, London.
26 April, '92

My dear Dr. Workman,

They tell me that in one month from today you will be 87 years of age. I can hardly believe it. It is not many weeks since I had the pleasure of an hour's conversation with you and I certainly did not find you old. No trace of senility in that acute, clear, questioning intellect that I have for so many years known so well.

Your friends are right to congratulate you for probably not one of themselves will see so great an age and if they do will hardly be in such excellent condition as that in which I saw you only the other day.

And really I do not see why you should not go on as you are indefinitely for I have seen no change in you in the last twenty years during which time many of us, with lesser endowments, have changed from young to old men.

Many years you have lived the honoured chief in your chosen country of our common specialty; many more years may you live, as you are today, the most learned and the most able of Canadian alienists. I am, dear Dr. Workman, your friend and admirer,

R. M. Bucke

*   *   *

156 Winchester Street,
Toronto, May 26, 1892

Dear Dr. Workman,

On this felicitous day (your Eighty-Seventh Birthday) kindly allow me to convey to you my heartiest congratulations and may you be spared many more happy years and continue to enjoy God's blessings with the unimpaired mental vigour so highly prized by all your professional and personal friends.

With expressions of respect and esteem I greatly value the friendship which has descended from my dear Father and Mother of fifty years duration.

My dear Wife also joins with me in good wishes to yourself and your family.

Yours sincerely,

Daniel Lamb.

*   *   *

Protestant Hospital for Insane
Montreal, 5th May, 1892

Dear Dr. Workman,

My heartiest greetings on you on the attainment of your 87th birthday, and my warmest congratulations that it finds you still in the full possession of your great mental powers, with undiminished enthusiasm in the study to which you have devoted your life, a study having for its object the amelioration of the condition of a class the most to be pitied of all God's poor afflicted ones.

Many there are who like myself feel gratefully proud to testify our obligations to you for aid and inspiration in our earlier studies; and none there be who can fail to appreciate the services and honour you have rendered to cultured scholarship and the advancement of the study of psychology. To me, personally, even from my birth, you have ever been the truest of friends, the wisest of counsellors; and whatever mode of success I have attained is largely due to the aid and advice of one who has been almost a second father to me, to one whose namesake I am more than proud to be.

"Words would but wrong the gratitude I owe you," so I'll e'en say no more than that it is my heartfelt prayer that many years may yet be added to the already long and useful life of one who has adorned our profession, even into hoary old age, "bearing" as the poet says, "the white blossoms of a blameless life."

Ever affectionately yours,

Thomas Joseph Workman Burgess.

*   *   *

Boston, May 9th, 1892.

My dear Dr. Workman,

We who have passed our eightieth birthday all know each other, as passengers do who have escaped from a shipwreck; they are acquaintances ever afterwards. And so, though I know you only by your high reputation, I venture to count myself among the friends who congratulate you on your eighty seventh birthday, hoping that you may live into the twentieth century, and as long in it as you find life worth living.

I am, my dear Sir,

Yours very respectfully and truly,

Oliver Wendell Holmes.

*   *   *

30 Daly Terrace
Stratford, May, 1892

Dear "Grandpa,"

It is a great pleasure to send congratulations and best wishes for a happy birthday. This month of May is the great anniversary month of the Workmans, and joys and sorrows have come strangely often to the family in this season of blossoms. It is a pleasant time of year to have a birthday, and in the beautiful Emerald Isle where Dame Nature is so lavish in bestowing her charms of the Springtime – you must have walked in the light when the outdoor world was looking its best. The song of birds, the hum of bees, gave a blithe welcome to the little lad, who proved to be in after years, such a blessing to his parents, and to all who in course of time came to bear his name – a good son – a good husband – a good father – and a good grandfather. All honour to you, – for your noble work in professional life, – for your high scholarly attainments, – for your lofty thoughts, and for your cheery companionship which has attracted so many friends, but these who are bound to you by family ties owe a still higher tribute to you for your worth, for the tender sympathy, unbounded love and extreme gentleness which have ever characterised your relations with them. Wishing you every blessing and happiness and with much love from all the Stratford branch.

Your loving daughter (my marriage)
Jane Workman.

*   *   *

Stratford, May 26th, 1892.

Dear Grandfather,

To-morrow will be your eighty-seventh birthday. I must not let it pass without writing you a letter, even if I do not write many letters to you during the year, I always manage to write one for your birthday.

We were all glad to hear, (from Aunt Jessie) that you were feeling much better. Auntie said that you wanted either Lillian or I to go down this summer. Mother has decided to let me go any time after school closes, on June 30th, that is if nothing happens to prevent the visit. Dolly will be up here this summer but unless we pass on the road I will not see her. Kitty is the one I always miss. I hope she is not going far this year so I will see her before or after she leaves the city.

We have been having dreadful weather here for the last week or two, it has rained every day. I went down to the little village of Tavistock last Friday night and did not return until last evening. I had a very enjoyable time considering the size of the place and the weather. We have posted you another box of flowers for a present. I hope they will arrive safe.

We have not had a letter from Colorado for some time but I think they are all well.

It seems such a short time since I was in Toronto last but it is a place a person is not likely to get tired of going to see. We wish you were able to come and see us. I hope you will be able to read French again this year. I enjoyed the reading very much last year and when I go down I will be glad to start again if you are able to. I will try and do some pronouncing myself. I hope that you will be able to write to us and tell me when it will be convenient for me to go down. Hoping to hear from someone soon I will now close,

Your loving Granddaughter,

Bessie F. Workman.

"Many Happy Returns of the Day." Love from ALL.   Elizth

*   *   *

APPENDIX THIRTEEN

OBITUARY POEM
(1894)

By K. S. McLean

IN MEMORY of the late Dr Joseph Workman, Student, Scientist, Reformer, Philanthropist and Humanitarian, chiefly distinguished for pioneer work among the insane.

> 0 thou who wast of that heroic mould,
> Student at once, and lover of mankind,
> Master and healer, whose prophetic mind,
> Amid the age-long darkness round them rolled,
> Found out a light and healing for the blind,
> Dumb captives of humanity grown cold,
> God's most unhappy children did'st unbind
> The clanking chain, and open wide the door
> Which greed and ignorance shall close no more:
> Though these, thy rescued captives cannot raise
> Statues and brasses graven with thy praise,
> Thy name like the world's heroes gone before
> Waits the sure justice of the coming days.

*   *   *

Notes

CHAPTER ONE

1. *Globe*, April 25, 1857.
2. Benjamin Workman, Personal Diary 1799-1859 (typed copy of a third of it in the possession of Christine Johnston, given by Judith and Elizabeth St. John, Toronto), p. 4.
3. George Rose, *A Cyclopedia of Canadian Biography* (Toronto: Rose, 1888), with quotations from A. S. Neale, *History of The Puritans*, Vol. I (1633), p. 452; and N. H. Darwin, *Irishmen in Canada*, p. 331.
4. G. Davies, *Encylopaedia Britannica, Vol.13* (Chicago, London, Toronto, Geneva: Benton, 1961), & Guizot, *Archbishop Laud and Priestly Government*.
5. B. Workman, Personal Diary, p. 4 (quoting Joseph Workman, Senior).
6. David Boyle, *Notes on the Life of Dr. Joseph Workman* (Toronto: Canadian Institute & Arbuthnot, 1894), p. 3; also Notes by Boyle printed in the *Alienist and Neurologist* (St. Louis, 1980), p. 2.
7. William Gilmore (Principal of the Ballymacash Public School, Northern Ireland), private conversation with author in Ballymacash, May, 1992.

CHAPTER TWO

1. D. Boyle, *Notes on the Life of Dr. Joseph Workman* (Toronto: Canadian Institute & Arbuthnot, 1894), p. 3; also in *Alienist and Neurologist* (St. Louis, 1980), p. 4.
2. Joseph Workman, *Weather Journals 1860-1894* (Environment Canada Library).
3. Boyle, *Notes on the Life of Dr. Joseph Workman*, p. 4.
4. Lillie and Thomas Workman, words written in 1911 on the back of a photo of the Ballymacash cottage, following a visit there in 1911.
5. William McMillan, private conversations held in Dunmurry, Northern Ireland, May, 1992. (The Rev. McMillan is the longterm minister of the Dunmurry Non-subscribing Presbyterian Church.)
6. B. Workman, Personal Diary 1799-1859, p. 31-32.

7. Ibid., p. 9.
8. Photos and letters from a trip to Ballymacash made by Thomas Workman, Joseph's son, and his wife, Lillie, c. 1911 (in the possession of John Haynes of Toronto); other descriptions from a trip made to Northern Ireland by the author in May, 1992.
9. C. Porter, R. McIlraith, J. Nelson, *Congregational Memoirs of the Presbyterian Congregations of Larne and Kilwaghter* (Larne: 1864, revised 1975).
10. W. McMillan, *Profiles in Courage, Biography of Rev. Dr. Henry Montgomery, 1788-1865* (Newry: 1975); J. Crozier, *The Life of Henry Montgomery* (London and Belfast: 1875), which includes: Henry Montgomery, *The Creed of an Arian*, Appendix F.
11. J. Jamieson, *History of the Royal Belfast Academical Institute 1810-1960* (Belfast: Wm. Mullen, 1980).
12. B. Workman, Personal Diary, p. 37.
13. Ibid., p. 37.

CHAPTER THREE

1. B. Workman, *Personal Diary 1799-1830*, p. 40-45.
2. Albert Horton, *History of the First Unitarian Congregation of Toronto 1845-1901* (Toronto: First Unitarian Congregation, 1901), p. 19: Quote: "Sir Henry Smith, at one time Speaker of the House of Assembly; the Hon. Lewis Walbridge, who also became Speaker; and the Hon. L. H. Horton, who was a prominent member of the Dominion Parliament."
3. Obituary re. Alexander Workman (Ottawa: The Free Press, 17 October, 1878).
4. J. Workman, Sr., *Notes on Family History;* also Fred J. Workman, *Workman Family History* (in the possession of John Haynes of Toronto).
5. J. Haegerty, *Four Centuries of Medical History, Vol. 1 & 2* (Toronto: MacMillan, 1928).
6. J. Workman, *Medical Inaugural Dissertation On Asiatic Cholera* (Montreal: McGill University, 1835), dedication on title page of published M.D. Thesis.
7. Edgar A. Collard, *History of the Unitarian Church of the Messiah* (Montreal: unpublished history in the church records, 1982), p. 71-72.
8. *Christian Guardian,* 20 August, 1834.
9. J. Workman, Medical Dissertation, p. 11-12.

10. Obituary re. Catharine Workman, *Notes on Family History* (records of Judith and Elizabeth St. John, Toronto).

11. S. Acheson, "The Workmans" in the *Proceedings of the Third Congress of the Scottish-Irish in America* (Toronto: 1891).

CHAPTER FOUR

1. Workman, Letter to Jarvis, November 1, 1855, *Edward Jarvis Letters 1853-1874* (Harvard Medical Library, Boston; also Griffin-Greenland collection, Queen Street Mental Health Centre Archives).

2. Wasnidge Family Records, (in the possession of John Haynes of Toronto); and C. Stogdill, "Joseph Workman, M.D., 1805-1894," *Canadian Medical Association Journal 95* (Toronto, 1966), p. 917.

3. Donald Jones, "Toronto Merchant became Father of Canadian Psychiatry," *Toronto Star,* May 2, 1981.

4. *Toronto Mirror*, Oct. 2, 1846.

5. Workman, *Casebooks 1847-49* (Academy of Medicine Collection, Thomas Fisher Rare Book Library, University of Toronto), entry of August 29 & 30, 1847.

6. William Canniff, *The Medical Profession in Upper Canada 1783-1850* (Toronto, 1894; repr. 1980), p. 668 & 671.

7. C. Godfrey, *Medicine for Ontario* (Belleville: Mika, 1979), p. 74.

8. W. T. Aikins, Letters to C. Widmer and J. Rolph, 1852 & 1853, *W. T. Aikins Collection* (Academy of Medicine Collection, Thomas Fisher Rare Book Library, University of Toronto), # 40, 52, 53, 54, 87, especially 54.

9. Workman, "Uterus," handwritten lecture (Academy of Medicine Collection, Thomas Fisher Rare Book Library, U. of T.), p. 29 & 32.

10. First Unitarian Congregation of Toronto, Funerals of 1857 (Church Archives).

11. Inquest on Mary Boyd held at the Provincial Lunatic Asylum, Toronto, 5th and 6th May 1868; Evidence and Correspondence in Full with Comments of the Toronto Press (Toronto, 1868), p. 14 and 22.

12. City of Toronto, "Minutes of the Council Meetings 1847-49" (City Hall Archives).

13. Governor General of Upper Canada, Montreal, Letter to J. Workman and Mayor re. concerns providing food and medical care for expected immigrants and re. establishment of a Board of Health, 1847 (Academy

of Medicine Collection, Thomas Fisher Rare Book Library, University of Toronto).

14. Workman, Statistics and Notes on "Toronto Emigrant Hospital June 1848-April 1849," in unpublished Lectures and Casebook (Academy of Medicine collection, Thomas Fisher Rare Book Library, University of Toronto).

15. Legislature of Ontario, *Royal Commission of Inquiry into the Affairs of King's College University and Upper Canada College, July 20, 1848*; Report of July 3, 1850; additional Report, 1852.

16. J. G. Hodgins, *The Documentary History of Education in Upper Canada 1791-1876 Vol. I* (Ontario Dpt. of Education), p. 211; Rev. John Strachan to John Macaulay, February 17, 1832, *Macaulay Papers* (Province of Ontario Archives).

17. Historical Sites and Monuments Board of Canada, Government of Canada, plaque on wall at University College.

18. C. Duncombe, "Report on the Subject of Prisons, Penitentiaries," *Journals of the Legislative Assembly of Upper Canada 1836*, Appendix 71.

CHAPTER FIVE

1. C. Duncombe, "Report on the Subject of Prisons, Penitentiaries," *Journals of the Legislative Assembly of Upper Canada 1836*, Appendix 71.

2. Rev. John Roaf, *Globe,* January 31, 1852. (N.B. *Globe* itself supported free schools.)

3. G. Barber, *Report of the Past History and Present Condition of the Common or Public Schools of the City of Toronto, Annual Reports 1850-1858* (Toronto: Lovell and Gibson, 1859), p. 33.

4. Ibid., p. 42-44, & p. 83-88.

5. Ibid., p. 103-104.

6. Workman, Personal Diary, March 23, 1869.

7. Workman, Pamphlet titled "Discourse on Education," lecture given in 1852 to the Mechanics Institute, later known as the Royal Canadian Institute; summary repr. in *The York Pioneer* (Toronto, 1967), p. 32-33. (Article available at the Toronto Board of Education Archives, and the handwritten original lecture available in the Academy of Medicine Collection, now in the Thomas Fisher Rare Book Library, University of Toronto.)

8. Ibid., p. 34.

9. Ibid., p. 33.

10. Staff of the Toronto Board of Education, under direction of E. A. Hardy, and H. Cochrane (editors), *Centennial Story 1850-1950* (Toronto: Nelson and Sons, 1950), p. 41.

11. Toronto Public School Board, "Minutes Oct. 16, 1850-Dec. 21, 1870" (Toronto Board of Education Archives), Minutes of March 21, 1852.

12. Workman, Personal Diary, August 10, 1881 (University of Toronto Archives).

CHAPTER SIX

1. Albert Horton, *History of the First Unitarian Congregation of Toronto 1845-1901* (Congregation's Archives), p. 1-18.

2. First Unitarian Congregation of Toronto, Minutes of Congregational Meeting, January 4, 1846.

3. Horton, History of First Unitarian Congregation, p. 11.

4. First Unitarian Congregation of Toronto, Minutes of the Board, 1853; also Workman's letters to Rev. Charles Dall, December 20, 1853; and to J. Bentley and the Board of Trustees, July 5, 1854 (First Unitarian Congregation Archives). N.B. The letters are reproduced in the Appendix.

5. C. Stogdill, "Joseph Workman, M.D., 1805-1894," *Canadian Medical Association Journal 95* (Toronto, 1966), p. 918.

6. Workman, "Demonomania and Witchcraft," *Journal of Insanity 1891*, p. 192-195.

7. Phillip Hewett, *Unitarians in Canada* (Toronto, 1995), p. 72-73.

8. Ben's silver writing desk was donated to the First Unitarian Congregation by Elizabeth and Judith St. John, Toronto, in 1978.

CHAPTER SEVEN

1. Thomas Brown, "Living with God's Afflicted: a history of the Provincial Lunatic Asylum of Toronto 1830-1911," Ph.D. Thesis, Queen's University (Kingston, 1981), p. 177-178.

2. E. Hounsom, "An Enormous Building for Its Time," *Journal of the Royal Architectural Society of Canada 42:6* (1965), p. 65.

3. R. L. Hector, *History of Ontario Hospital Queen Street 1841-1854* (Griffin-Greenland collection, Queen Street Mental Health Centre, Toronto: 1961), p. 6.

4. Christopher Widmer, Letter to John Rolph, April 1, 1854, *W. T. Aikens*

Papers (Academy of Medicine collection, Thomas Fisher Rare Book Library, University of Toronto).

5. H. E. MacDermot, *The History of the Canadian Medical Association* (Toronto, 1935), p. 161.

6. C. Widmer, Letter to J. Workman, Nov. 15, 1853 (Griffin-Greenland Collection, Queen Street Mental Health Centre Archives; also Academy of Medicine collection, Thomas Fisher Rare Book Library, University of Toronto).

7. Robert Burns, Letter to J. Workman, Nov. 26, 1853 (Griffin-Greenland Collection, Queen Street Mental Health Centre Archives; also Academy of Medicine collection, Thomas Fisher Rare Book Library, University of Toronto).

8. H. E. MacDermot, *One Hundred Years of Medicine in Canada, 1867-1967* (Toronto, 1967), p. 36-37; *The History of the Canadian Medical Association* (Toronto: 1935), p. 161.

9. Workman, "A Description of the Pestilent Condition of the Toronto Lunatic Asylum in 1853, and the Means Adopted to Remove It," *Sanitary Journal 2* (Toronto: 1876), p. 3.

10. Workman, "Report of the Medical Superintendent of the Provincial Lunatic Asylum at Toronto 1853-4," Appendix to *Journals of the Legislative Assembly of the Province of Canada* 1854 *No.1*, p. 5.

11. Workman, *Sanitary Journal 2*, p. 4.

12. Ibid., p. 35.

13. Workman, "Annual Address at the Canadian Medical Association 1878," p. 4-8.

14. Ibid., p. 6.

15. Eric Arthur, *No Mean City* (Toronto, 1964), p. 82.

16. Workman, *Sanitary Journal 2*, p. 3.

17. Workman, Letter to C. K. Clarke in 1891, *Clarke Papers*.

18. John Howard, Diary re. March 29, 1853, *Howard Papers 1830-1890* (Metro Toronto Reference Library).

19. Jill Franklin, "Howard's Foray into Lunacy," *High Park 3: 4* (Toronto, 1996), p. 9.

20. Workman, Letter to C. K. Ckarke in 1891, *Clarke Papers*.

21. Workman, "Report of the Medical Superintendent of the Provincial Lunatic Asylum at Toronto 1853-4," Appendix to *Journals of the Legislative*

Assembly of the Province of Canada 1854, p. 10; also similar theme in "Annual Report 1856," p. 27.

22. Margaret Atwood, *Alias Grace* (Toronto, 1996), p. 48-49 and p. 464-465.

23. Workman, "Report of the Medical Superintendent of the Provincial Lunatic Asylum at Toronto 1873," Appendix to *Journals of the Legislative Assembly of the Province of Canada 1873,* p. 19.

24. Workman, "Address to Medical Students, 1883" (*Matrix* collection, Queen Street Mental Health Centre, 1980), p. 1.

25. Workman, Letters sent to Jarvis, *Edward Jarvis Papers 1853-1874* (Countway Library, Harvard University), especially November 1, 1855.

26. Workman, "Notes of a Visit to Lunatic Asylums in Great Britain and Ireland," *American Journal of Insanity 16* (1860), p. 278-280.

27. R. Bahre, "Joseph Workman and Lunacy Reform: humanitarian or moral entrepreneur?" *Canadian Historical Association* (Montreal, 1980), p. 33-36.

28. *Globe*, February 11, 19, 24; March 2; April 25; May 12, 1857.

29. Chris Raible, "999 Queen Street West: The Toronto Asylum Scandal," *The Beaver* (Toronto, March-April, 1994), p. 43-44; also the *Globe*, April 25, 1857.

30. Workman Family History, and conversations with John C. Haynes (St. Catharine's, Ontario, 1982).

31. Workman, Letters to William Lyon Mackenzie, September 1, 1852, March 8 and 31, July 9, August 6, December 1, 1855; March 2, 10 and 19, 1857, *Mackenzie-Lindsey Papers, Correspondence*(Archives of Ontario); also Chris Raible, "Case History/Notes et dossiers de recherche. 'Your daughter & I Are Not Likely To Quarrel': Notes on a dispute between Joseph Workman and William Lyon Mackenzie," *Canadian Bulletin of Medical History 11:2* (1994), p. 387-395.

CHAPTER EIGHT

1. D. Hake Tuke, *The Insane in the United States and Canada* (London: 1885), p. 216. (repr. New York, 1973).

2. R. Baehre, "Joseph Workman and Lunacy Reform: humanitarian or moral entrepreneur?" Paper presented to the *Canadian Historical Society* (Montreal: 1980), p. 16.

3. Ibid., p. 1.

4. R. Baehre, "The ill-regulated mind: the making of psychiatry in Ontario 1830-1921," Ph.D. Thesis, York University (Toronto: 1985), Ch. 11: p. 1.

5. T. Brown, *Dictionary of Canadian Biography XII* (Toronto: 1990), p. 1126.

6. T. Brown, "Living with God's Afflicted: a History of the Provincial Lunatic Asylum at Toronto 1830-1911," Ph.D. Thesis, Queen's University (Kingston, 1981), p. 165.

7. Ibid., p 232.

8. Workman, "Report of the Medical Superintendent of the Provincial Lunatic Asylum at Toronto 1866-68" (known hereafter as "Annual Report"), *Journals of the Legislative Assembly of the Province of Canada*, Sessional Papers, (hereafter known as J. L. A. P. C.), p. 9.

9. Workman, "On Temperance," lecture written in early 1850s (Academy of Medicine collection, Thomas Fisher Rare Book Library, University of Toronto), p. 6.

10. Ibid., p. 64.

11. Ibid., p. 66.

12. Workman, "Proceedings of the Annual Meeting of the Association of Medical Superintendents of American Insane Institutions 1863," *American Journal of Insanity 19* (1862-63), p. 68.

13. Workman, "Annual Report 1854-56," Appendix 2, p. 27-28.

14. Workman, Letter to Jarvis, January 30, 1868, *Edward Jarvis Papers* (Griffin-Greenland collection, Queen Street Mental Health Centre Archives).

15. Workman, "Insanity from Hunger, Fear, and Suffering,"*American Journal of Insanity 2* (1845-46), p. 190; "Starvation and Insanity," *Am. J. Insanity 24* (1867-8), p. 482.

16. Workman, "Annual Report 1853-4," Appendix H, p. 15.

17. Workman, "Proceedings of the Annual Meeting of the Association of Medical Superintendents of American Institutions for the Insane," *Am. J. of Insanity 15* (1858), p. 105.

18. Workman, "Annual Report 1858," Appendix 9 p. 13.

19. Workman, "Annual Report 1869," p. 19.

20. Workman, "Annual Report 1860," p. 22.

21. Workman, "Annual Report 1858," p. 15.

22. Workman, "Annual Report 1862," p. 7.

23. J. Workman, "Insanity of the Religious-Emotional Type, and its occasional physical relations," *American Journal of Insanity 26* (1869), p. 39-43.

24. Workman,"Insanity and Crime," *Canada Lancet 9* (1876), p. 6; Muncie case is also described in *Workman's Asylum Journals 1871-1875* (Academy of Medicine Collection, Thomas Fisher Rare Book Library, University of Toronto Library), March 8, 1873.

25. Workman, "Proceedings of the Annual Meeting of the Association of Medical Superintendents of American Institutions for the Insane." *Am. J. of Insanity 15* (1858), p. 81.

26. Workman, "Annual Report 1863," p. 7; Also 1864, Sessional Paper 39; & 1866, S. P. 6; "Observations on Insanity" *Can. Med. Journal 1* (1865), p. 405.

CHAPTER NINE

1. Workman, "On Crime and Insanity," *Transactions of the Canadian Medical Association 1877*, p. 85-89.

2. Workman, "Moral Insanity – What is it?" *American Journal of Insanity* 1883, p. 341.

3. Workman, "Annual Report 1863," *J. L. A. P. C.* Sessional Papers 66.

4. Workman, "On Crime and Insanity" (1877), p. 82

5. Workman, "Annual Report 1861," p. 2.

6. Thomas Burgess, "Canadian Institutions for the Insane,"*Procedures and Transactions of the Royal Society Of Canada 4* (1898), p. 30.

7. Workman, "The Public Care of the Insane and the Management of Asylums," *Alienist and Neurologist* (July, 1884), p. 492-496.

8. Ibid., p. 498.

9. J. Langmuir, "Annual Report of Inspector 1875," *J. L. A. P. C.* Sessional Papers 4, p.4.

10. Workman, "Notes on a Visit to Lunatic Asylums in Great Britain and Ireland," *American Journal of Insanity, 16* (Jan. 1860), p. 283.

11. Workman, "Annual Report 1858"*J. L. A. P. C.* Appendix 9, p. 17-18.

12. Burgess, *Canadian Institutions for the Insane*, p. 30.

13. Workman, Letters to William Lyon Mackenzie, March 2, 1857, *Mackenzie-Lindsey Papers, Correspondence* (Archives of Ontario); also Chris Raible, "Case History/Notes et dossiers de recherche. 'Your daughter & I Are Not Likely To Quarrel': Notes on a dispute between Joseph Workman and William Lyon Mackenzie," *Canadian Bulletin of Medical History 11:2* (1994), p. 387-395

14. "Proceedings of the Annual Meeting of the Association of Medical Superintendents of American Institutions for the Insane,"*American Journal of Insanity 27* (1871), p. 341.
15. D. Boyle, "Joseph Workman, M. D.," *Alienist and Neurologist* (St. Louis, Jan. 1890), p. 1.
16. Cyril Greenland, "Three Pioneers of Canadian Psychiatry," *Journal of the American Medical Association 200* (June 1967), p. 835.

CHAPTER TEN

1. *Asylum Journals (1871-1875)* are available at the Academy of Medicine collection, Thomas Fisher Rare Book Library, University of Toronto Library. *The Personal Diaries (1867-1893)* belong to the University of Toronto Archives, with typed excerpts in the Academy of Medicine collection, Thomas Fisher Rare Book Library, University of Toronto Library. Alfred Lavell, Provincial Archivist in 1922, has added notes. The two volumes of personal diaries disappeared for a while but were found in Dr. C. K. Clarke's papers by his son Dr. Eric Clarke in 1922 and donated to the Dean of Medicine, for the University of Toronto. *The Weather Journals (1860-1894)* are at the Library of Environment Canada, Toronto.
2. Personal Diary, January 14, 1870.
3. Workman, Letter to Edward Jarvis, July 22, 1871 (Griffin-Greenland collection, Queen Street Mental Health Centre Archives).
4. D. Boyle, "Obituary Notes on Dr. Joseph Workman," Speech at the Canadian Institute (Toronto, 1894), p. 6.
5. I. Macalpine, & R. Hunter, *George III and the Mad Business* (Penguin, 1969), quoting Workman, from the "Proceedings at the Annual Meeting of the Association of Medical Superintendents of American Institutions for the Insane," *Journal of Insanity* (July 1855); also Workman, "Speech to Medical Students in Toronto, 1883" (in the *Matrix* collection, Queen Street Mental Health Centre Archives, Toronto), p. 1.
7. Ibid., p. 1.

CHAPTER ELEVEN

1. *The Weather Journals (1860-1894)* are at the Library of Environment Canada, Toronto. After Joseph's death few people knew where they were

to be found. But on July 12, 1922, Professor C. F. Lavelle presented four leather-bound weather journals to Sir Francis Stupart, Head of the Meteorological Service of Canada. Professor Lavelle had married Katherine (Kitty) Kennedy, a granddaughter of Joseph. The records were nearly lost again when the contents of the Library of the Meteorological Services were scattered in basements and warehouses for 23 years until the new building was ready in 1971. The volumes were about to be thrown out when Morley Thomas, Director of the Canadian Climatic Centre of Environment Canada, recognized their worth and rescued them. This information was provided by Mr. Thomas in October, 1980.

2. S. Sommerville, "Dr. Workman's Weather Journal," *Chinook 1979* (winter), p. 20-21.

3. M. K. Thomas, "A Century of Canadian Meteorology," *Annual Records of Operations, Atmospheric Environment Service, 1971-1972* (Environment Canada), p. 1-6.

4. Sommerville, p.20.

CHAPTER TWELVE

1. Workman, Letter to Jarvis July 23, 1874 *Edward Jarvis Papers 1853-74* (Harvard University Archives and Queen Street Mental Health Centre Archives).

2. Ibid., (re. Ben) July 23, 1874, and (re. himself) July 22, 1871.

3. Cyril Greenland, "C. K. Clarke, a Founder of Canadian Psychiatry," *Canadian Medical Association Journal 95* (July, 1966), p. 156.

4. Workman, "Address given to Toronto Medical Students, 1883," (reprinted in *Matrix,* 1980, Queen Street Mental Health Centre and available in the Archives).

5. Workman, "Crime and Insanity." *Transactions of the Canadian Medical Society* 1876, p. 18.

6. Workman, "Discourse on Education," (article, Toronto Board of Education Archives; hand-written copy of lecture given in 1852 in the Academy of Medicine Collection, Thomas Fisher Rare Book Library, University of Toronto).

7. Workman, "Crime and Insanity," Transactions of the Canadian Medical Association 1876, *Canadian Lancet 9* (1876-77), p. 18 & 21.

8. Workman, "Case of Erastus Hotchkiss," *American Journal of Insanity* 1876.

9. Workman, "On Crime and Insanity," Transactions of the Canadian Medical Association 1877, *Canada Lancet 9* (1876-77).

10. Ibid., p. 84.

11. Workman, "Case 3, (Meisner-Lyons case)," (*Matrix* collection, Queen Street Mental Health Centre, 1850-52).

12. Ibid., "Case 6," (*Matrix* collection).

13. Ibid., "Case 5;" also an article by an unidentified author: "Sleuthing by Dr. Workman," *Eloquent Mystery Magazine* (Toronto: 1970).

14. Inquest on Mary Boyd held at the Provincial Lunatic Asylum, Toronto, 5th and 6th May 1868; Evidence and Correspondence in Full with Comments of the Toronto Press (Toronto, 1868).

15. Workman, "Case 4," (*Matrix* collection).

16. Workman, "Demonomania and Witchcraft," *American Journal of Insanity, 1871*, p. 175-193.

17. Workman, "Case 2 (Mary Ward)," (*Matrix* collection).

18. Workman, "Proceedings of the Thirteenth Annual Meeting of the Association of Medical Superintendents of American Institutions for the Insane," *American Journal of Insanity 15* (July, 1858), p. 80.

19. Workman, "Past, Present and Future," Lecture at 51st Session of the McGill Medical Faculty (Montreal, 1883). (N. B. Joseph was their oldest living graduate at that time.) Also available in an untitled book of annual reports and articles (reproduced by George Rose, 1890; and available in the Queen Street Mental Health Centre Archives), p. 9-12.

20. Workman, "Address to Students 1883," (*Matrix* collection at Queen Street Mental Health Centre; reproduced in 1980).

CHAPTER THIRTEEN

1. Workman, "Proceedings of the Toronto Medical Society," *Canadian Lancet 10* (1878), p. 316.

2. Workman, Letter to Dr. J. G. Hyde, November 12, 1868, *Hyde Letters* and reprinted in the article by Peter Mithram, "'Very Truly and Undisturbedly Yours:' Joseph Workman and a Verdict of Malprcatice against John Galbraith Hyde," *Canadian Bulletin of Medical History 13* (1996), p. 139-149.

3. Testimonials are in the Griffin-Greenland Collection at the Queen Street Mental Health Centre.

4. Most of these letters can be found in the Academy of Medicine collection

at the Thomas Fisher Rare Book Library, University of Toronto.

CHAPTER FOURTEEN

1. E. A. Collard, *History of the Church of the Messiah, the Montreal Congrega-tion* (unpublished document in the possession of the Montreal congrega-tion), p. 106.
2. Workman, Personal Diary, February 13, 1871 (University of Toronto Ar-chives).
3. Collard, *History of Unitarian Church in Montreal*, p.106.
4. G. Tulchinsky, "William Workman," *Dictionary of Canadian Biography 10, 1871-1880* (Toronto, 1972), p. 717.
5. A. Cook, "Ancient chapel built here for spite still stands as a reminder of bygone feuds, *Montreal Daily Star,* August 12, 1937, (in the possession of John Haynes of Toronto).
6. Parchment addressed to Dr. Benjamin Workman, (Baldwin Room col-lection, Toronto Reference Library).
7. Elizabeth Workman, letter to their son, William, dated July 25, 1854, (in the possession of John Haynes of Toronto).
8. Workman, "Medical Inaugural Dissertation on Asiatic Cholera," (pub-lished Thesis for M.D. degree, Montreal: McGill University, 1835), p. 44, (also available at the Thomas Fisher Rare Book Library, University of Toronto).
9. Notes in the *Matrix* 1981 Collection of the Queen Street Mental Health Centre.
10. Obituary, *Stratford Evening Beacon,* June 24, 1896; and *Evening Herald*, June 25, 1896.
11. Elizabeth Workman, Letter to their son, William, dated March 8, 1859; and J. Workman, Letter to the widow of Joseph Wasnidge, dated Octo-ber 15, 1861 (both letters are in the possession of John Haynes of To-ronto).
12. Workman, Letter to Jane Clarke, dated August 4, 1872 (in the possession of John Haynes of Toronto).
13. Workman, Personal Diary, entry dated May 26, 1886.

CHAPTER FIFTEEN

1. Cyril Greenland, "C. K. Clarke, A Founder of Canadian Psychiatry," *Canadian Medical Journal 95* (July, 1966), p. 835.

2. C. K. Clarke, Obituary Notes on Dr. Joseph Workman, 1894, p. 3.

3. H. E. MacDermot, *One Hundred Years of Medicine in Canada 1867-1967* (Toronto, 1967), p. 36.

4. W. Canniff, *Medical Profession in Upper Canada 1800-1850* (Toronto, 1895), p. 669.

5. Workman, "On Temperance," lecture written in 1850s (Academy of Medicine Collection, Thomas Fisher Rare Book Library, U. of T.), p. 69.

6. Workman, Letter to Edward Jarvis, July 22, 1871 (Griffin-Greenland Collection, Queen Street Mental Health Centre Archives).

7. D. Boyle, "Obituary Notes on Dr. Joseph Workman," speech at the Canadian Institute (Toronto,1894), p. 6.

APPENDIX ONE

1. Ben Workman, Diary, p. 4 (quoting his father, Joseph Workman, Senior).

2. David Boyle, *Notes on the Life of Dr. Joseph Workman* (Toronto: Canadian Institute & Arbuthnot, 1894), p. 3; also Notes printed in the *Alienist and Neurologist* (St. Louis, 1980), p. 2.

3. Mary (Madie) Graves, John (Jack) Hyatt, John C. Haynes, private conversations and correspondence (Sharbot Lake, Montreal, and St. Catharine's, Ontario, 1981 & 1982).

4. Joseph Workman, Senior, *Notes of Family History,* & Fred J. Workman, *Workman Family History* (in the possession of John Haynes of Toronto).

5. Ben Workman, Diary, p. 5 (quoting Joseph Workman, Senior).

6. Ibid., p. 1.

7. Ibid., p. 3.

8. Boyle, Notes, p. 4.

9. T. Hornberger, *Encyclopaedia Britannica Vol. 9* (Chicago, London, Toronto, Geneva: Benton, 1961).

10. Workman Family Tree, (one is in the possession of John Haynes of Toronto, and another was provided by Ross Workman of Victoria, B.C.).

APPENDIX FIVE

1. Ben Workman, Diary, p. 30-31.

2. Ibid., p. 50.

3. Ibid., p. 46.

4. Phillip Hewett, *Unitarians in Canada* (Toronto: Canadian Unitarian Council, 1995), p. 40-54; also Mary Lu MacDonald, Letter to Christine Johnston, 1981.

5. Hewett, *Unitarians in Canada,* p. 42.

6. Obituary re. Catharine Workman, *Notes on Family History* (records of Judith and Elizabeth St. John, Toronto).

7. Ben Workman, *Personal Ledger 1847-1875* (First Unitarian Congregation of Toronto Archives), 1850-1855, especially 1852.

8. Edgar Collard, *History of Unitarian Church of the Messiah, Montreal,* p. 103.

9. Albert Horton, *History of First Unitarian Congregation of Toronto 1845-1901,* p. 20.

10. Collard, *History,* p. 92 & p. 120.; also Hewett *Unitarians in Canada*, p. 40. Hewett quotes the Rev. Charles Dall: "All such rally around Benjamin Workman, who is a noble Christian if ever there was one."

11. *Notes on the Family History of Benjamin Workman* (records of Judith and Elizabeth St. John, Toronto).

Bibliography

Journals and Newspapers of the Period

JOURNALS:

Canadian Medical Journal (1864-1883).

Canadian Lancet (1880-1890).

American Journal of Insanity (1855-1883).

Alienist and Neurologist (1884-1894).

NEWSPAPERS:

Mirror, became the *Toronto Mirror* (1837-1857).

Globe (1850-1880).

Books

Arthur, Eric. *No Mean City*. Toronto: University of Toronto Press, 1964.

Canniff, William. *The Medical Profession in Upper Canada 1783-1850*. Toronto: 1894; repr. 1980.

Collard, Edgar A. *History of the Unitarian Church of the Messiah*. Montreal: unpublished history in the church records, 1982.

Crozier, J. *The Life of Henry Montgomery*. London and Belfast: 1875; which includes: Henry Montgomery. *The Creed of an Arian*, Appendix F.

Hardy, E. A. and staff of the Toronto Board of Education, under direction of Hardy, E. A. and Cochrane, H. (editors). *Centennial Story 1850-1950*. Toronto: Nelson and Sons, 1950.

Hewett, Phillip. *Unitarians in Canada*. Toronto: Canadian Unitarian Council, 1995.

Hodgins, J. G. *The Documentary History of Education in Upper Canada 1791-1876 I*. Ontario, Dpt. of Education.

Horton, Albert. *History of the First Unitarian Congregation of Toronto 1845-1901*. Toronto: Church Archives, 1901.

Jamieson, J. *History of the Royal Belfast Academical Institute 1810-1960*. Belfast: Wm. Mullen, 1980.

MacDermot, H. E. *One Hundred Years of Medicine in Canada 1867-1967*. Toronto: 1967.

—— *The History of the Canadian Medical Association*. Toronto: 1935.

McMillan, William. *Profiles in Courage, Biography of Rev. Dr. Henry Montgomery, 1788-1865*. Newry: 1975.

Rose, George. *A Cyclopedia of Canadian Biography*. Toronto: Rose, 1888.

Tuke, D. Hake. *The Insane in the United States and Canada*. London: 1885; repr. New York:1973.

Articles on Dr. Joseph Workman

Baehre, Rainer. "Joseph Workman and Lunacy Reform: humanitarian or moral entrepreneur?" Paper presented to the *Canadian Historical Society* (Montreal: 1980).

Brown, Thomas. *Dictionary of Canadian Biography XII* (1990), p. 1126.

Boyle, David. "Joseph Workman, M. D." *Alienist and Neurologist* (St. Louis: Jan. 1890).

Edginton, Barry. "The Well-Ordered Body: The Quest for Sanity through Nineteenth-Century Asylum Architecture." *Canadian Bulletin of Medical History 11* (1994), p. 375-386.

Greenland, Cyril. "Three Pioneers of Canadian Psychiatry." *Journal of the American Medical Association 200* (June 1967).

Johnston, Christine. "The Irish Connection: Benjamin and Joseph and their Brothers, and their Coats of many Colours." Paper presented to the Canadian Unitarian Universalist Historical Society (Montreal, 1982).

Jones, Donald. "Toronto Merchant became Father of Canadian Psychiatry." *Toronto Star,* May 2, 1981.

Mitham, Peter. "Artifacts and Archives. 'Very Truly and Undisturbedly Yours': Joseph Workman and a Verdict of Malpractice against John Galbraith Hyde." *Canadian Bulletin of Medical History 13* (1996), p. 139-149.

Raible, Chris. "999 Queen Street West: The Toronto Asylum Scandal." *The Beaver* (March-April, 1994).

—— "Case History/Notes et dossiers de recherche. 'Your daughter & I Are Not Likely To Quarrel': Notes on a dispute between Joseph Workman and William Lyon Mackenzie." *Canadian Bulletin of Medical History 11:2* (1994), p. 387-395

Stogdill, C. G. "Joseph Workman, M.D., 1805-1894." *Canadian Medical Association Journal 95* (1966).

Doctoral Theses

Baehre, R. *The ill-regulated mind: the making of psychiatry in Ontario 1830-1921*. Ph.D. Thesis, York University, 1985: Ch.11.

Brown, T. *Living with God's Afflicted: a History of the Provincial Lunatic Asylum at Toronto 1830-1911.* Ph.D. Thesis, Queen's University, Kingston, 1981.

Moran, J. *Insanity, the Asylum and Society in Nineteenth Century Quebec and Ontario.* Ph.D. Thesis, York University, 1998.

Diaries and Letters

Aikins, W. T. Letters to C. Widmer and J. Rolph, 1852 & 1853. *W. T. Aikins Collection, No. 40, 52, 53, 54, 87.* (Academy of Medicine Collection, Thomas Fisher Rare Book Library, University of Toronto.)

Clarke, Lieut.-Col. Charles. Letters to and from J. Workman. *Clarke Papers.* (Ontario Archives.)

Clarke, Dr. Charles K. Letters to and from J. Workman. *Clarke Papers.* (Clarke Institute Archives, Toronto.)

Howard, John. Diary. *Howard Papers 1830-1890.* (Metro Toronto Reference Library.)

Jarvis, Edward. Letters to and from J. Workman. *Edward Jarvis Letters, 1853-1874.* (Harvard Medical Library, Boston; also Griffin-Greenland collection, Queen Street Mental Health Centre Archives.)

Mackenzie, William Lyon. Letters to and from J. Workman. *Mackenzie-Lindsey Papers, Correspondence.* (Archives of Ontario.)

Workman, Benjamin. Personal Diary 1799-1859. (Typed copy of a third of it in the possession of Christine Johnston, given by Judith and Elizabeth St. John, Toronto; another copy in the possession of John Haynes of Toronto.)

Workman, Fred J. *Workman Family History.* (In the possession of John Haynes of Toronto.)

Workman, Joseph, Sr. *Notes of Family History.* (In the possession of John Haynes of Toronto.)

Workman, Dr. Joseph. *Asylum Journals 1872-1875.* (Academy of Medicine Collection, Thomas Fisher Rare Book Library, University of Toronto Library.)

——*Personal Diaries 1867-1894* (The University of Toronto Archives, with typed excerpts in the Academy of Medicine Collection, Thomas Fisher Rare Book Library, University of Toronto. Alfred Lavell, Provincial Archivist in 1922, has added notes.)

—— *Weather Journals 1860-1894*. (Library of Environment Canada, Toronto.)

Institutional Records

City of Toronto Archives (1847-1850).

First Unitarian Congregation of Toronto Archives (1845-1898).

Globe and Mail Archives (1846-1883)

Legislature of Ontario, *Royal Commission of Inquiry into the Affairs of King's College University and Upper Canada College, July 20, 1848*; Report of July 3, 1850; additional Report, 1852.

—— Reports of the Medical Superintendent of the Provincial Lunatic Asylum at Toronto, 1850-1867. *Journals of the Legislative Assembly of the Province of Canada, (J.L.A.P.C.)* Sessional Papers.

—— Reports of the Medical Superintendent of the Provincial Lunatic Asylum at Toronto, 1867-1871. *(J.L.A.P.C.)*

—— Reports of the Medical Superintendent of the Asylum for the Insane, Toronto. *(J.L.A.P.C.)*

—— Reports of the Inspector of Asylums and Prisons. (J. Langmuir, 1867-1875.)

Queen Street Mental Health Centre Archives (Griffin-Greenland Collection, and items collected from their *Matrix* newsletter).

Toronto Board of Education Archives (1850-1854).

University of Toronto Archives (1856-1894).

Collections of Dr. Joseph Workman's Unpublished Works

Griffin-Greenland Collection, Queen Street Mental Health Centre Archives, Toronto.

Academy of Medicine Collection, Thomas Fisher Rare Book Library, University of Toronto Library.

Index